I Died on the Titanic

by

Monica O'Hara - Keeton

There is only one person to whom this book could possibly be dedicated: my wonderful husband, Joe Keeton, who made it - and so much more - possible!

* * * * * *

First published 1996 by Countyvise Limited, 1 & 3 Grove Road, Rock Ferry, Birkenhead, Wirral, Merseyside L42 3XS.

P.O. Box 52, Hoylake, Wirral, Merseyside, England L47 0NT.
Tel/Fax: 0151-632 6346.

ISBN 0 907768 86 5

Contents

Foreword

by

Roy Stemman

(i)

The passage of time has done little to diminish the understandable fascination which the terrible Titanic disaster has had for generations. There have been other human tragedies involving even greater loss of life, but the horror of that ill-fated voyage seems to be imprinted on the human psyche. Few, today, are not aware of the claims made for the Titanic before her maiden voyage or of the appalling reality when she hit an iceberg.

Countless books have been written about that dreadful night. Films and television documentaries have added their interpretations of the event. And survivors' stories have appeared in many publications and numerous languages. Recently, modern technology has made it possible to explore and film the wreckage of the luxurious liner on the bed of the Atlantic and to see again everyday objects which went down with her into the freezing waters.

So, it might be thought that there is nothing new to say about the Titanic.

Monica O'Hara proves this is not the case in a way that is both challenging and entertaining. For this is an eye-witness account of the sinking of the Titanic, not by a survivor but by one of its victims.

What we learn is that from an early age she has had memories which she could not understand until experiencing a hypnotic regression and discovering that in a previous life she had been one of the Titanic's passengers.

Some readers - perhaps the majority - might find that difficult to accept, in which case they will be relieved to discover that Monica O'Hara is the perfect narrator for this extraordinary story. She understands their scepticism and treats much of the material received during the hypnotic regression sessions with great caution. She is also aware that it is easy to underestimate the power of the mind and to make the false assumption that what appears to be impossible must therefore be "magical" or paranormal.

In many ways, however, this book is not about the Titanic at all. It is a story about human love and emotion; of passion, obstinacy and fickleness, too, pieced together like a riveting detective story. The author takes us with her on her voyage of discovery into the past, showing us the pieces of the jigsaw as she uncovers them and putting them together until a picture emerges that contains as many surprises for her as it does for us. The fact that the person she recalls being in her previous life is so different to her present personality - Monica O'Hara does not disguise her dislike of the young woman - adds to the fascination of her narrative.

If what the author has experienced were unique it would, perhaps, be reasonable for us to resist the conclusion she draws. But there is a growing body of evidence for reincarnation which supports her claim very powerfully. I am familiar with many hundreds of similar cases in which individuals have been able to recall a previous life in varying degrees of detail and accuracy. Some concern young children who begin talking of their earlier life, naming their partners, their children and even the village in which they lived, almost from the moment they are able to speak. For others, such memories are largely dormant until brought to the surface by hypnosis or some similar technique which apparently lifts the veil between this life and the previous one.

Taken as a whole, I believe these cases provide convincing evidence that we live more lives than one and that it is to help us develop spiritually that we are reborn. I am also convinced that it is only a matter of time before the weight of testimony such as Monica O'Hara's will persuade people at large that there is another dimension to the existence we lead and a purpose to our lives.

The irony is that huge amounts of money have been spent to probe the ocean's depths and photograph the broken shell of the Titanic, and there has even been talk of raising it to the surface. Monica O'Hara, on the other hand, demonstrates that there are other ways of shedding light on history which may have far more relevance for the majority of us. Just think how much more we would know about human nature if a similar sum of money were spent on exploring the mysteries of the mind .... and the possibility of reincarnation, in particular. That's precisely what this book invites you to do.

Roy Stemman,
Editor,
Reincarnation International Magazine
March 1996

Foreword

by
John P. Eaton
(ii)

Titanic yields her secrets grudgingly.

Days passed before details of the night of terror were published in detail.

Weeks passed before the completion of two formal investigations into the wreck's cause; months went by before the inquiries' results were made known.

Years passed before official records of the British inquiry were made available to public scrutiny. Even more time elapsed before American court records yielded to researchers the myriad details of the hearings for limitation of liability for **Titanic's** owners.

And it was not until August 1985, more than 70 years after the disaster that the wreck was discovered.

Even after discovery, **Titanic** did not give up her secrets easily. The wreck lies in what is perhaps the most hostile environment to man anywhere on earth: approximately 350 miles southeast of Newfoundland; 2½ miles straight down to total blackness, pressure of more than three tons per sq in and water temperature approaching 0°C.

After its discovery, the wreck was explored briefly in 1985, then in more detail during an expedition the following year. A joint American-French expedition in 1987 resulted in not only additional photographs and motion picture film but also retrieval of a number of objects from the debris field - an area on the sea bottom around the wreck itself, in which a large amount of **Titanic's** contents were strewn when the ship struck bottom.

In July 1991 the wreck was filmed in superb detail by a Canadian film company. The breathtaking results are seen in the commercial film **Titanica**, which unfortunately requires a special screen and projector for viewing.

Additional examinations of the wreck site and its debris field followed in 1993 and 1994, again with retrieval of objects and artefacts. Future expeditions are planned.

Because of the great depth at which the wreck lies, each dive requires unwavering control, strictest observance of safety regulations, highly specialised equipment that is constructed at great cost and operated by specially trained and skilled technicians. Divers to the wreck are in extreme peril every moment of each dive; they must place utmost confidence in the equipment's integrety and trust in the dive team's proficiency. Even photographic equipment and lights must be protected from the immense pressure. Retrieval equipment must be designed to accommodate the special circumstances.

Even when the historically priceless and physically beautiful objects are retrieved and brought to the surface, there are difficulties in stablising, conserving and preserving the objects' viability. Chemistry, electrolysis, and all the iles of the historical archaeologist's skill are incorporated into rescuing the objects from deterioration, allowing them to be safely stored and, later, exhibited.

Titanic yields her secrets grudging!

Even after the wreck's discovery; even after the exploration; even after the objects are once again available, enabling scientists and historians to examine the disaster in new perspectives...Even after we have **seen** the wreck and some of its startling contents.. There are still mysteries, still some aspects of the disaster, circumstances whose detail are lacking, questions whose answers may never be known.

Not the least of these concerns relates to **Titanic's** passengers. Just as five apparent unrelated people were killed in the fictional account of the collapse of the bridge of San Luis Rey, so the 2,228 real people aboard **Titanic** were gathered together by circumstance to be at a particular spot aboard a particular ship at a particular time.

What was it that brought these people together? More enigmatic, what was it that kept many people away from the voyage that caused some to cancel reservations and others to avoid the journey altogether? These are questions that can not now be answered objectively. Yet, they continue to persist.

I will not discuss in this brief introduction my impression of the methodology of regressive hypnosis used by Mònica O'Hara, the author, and her hypnotherapist husband Joe Keeton, in achieving entry into history's flow. Nor will I interfere with a cracking good detective story and reveal how their apparently valid conclusions were achieved.

I will say only this: that I observed a fragment of the work in progress; I personally saw the technique of regression in use. And I have no reason to doubt what my eye saw and my ear heard.

Monica O'Hara's search for Lucie and friends takes us on a road with many twists and turns, many crossroads, but no real dead ends. Each path, each corridor, each opening door provides some progress.

By journey's end, we have made the acquaintance of two fascinating new characters and their own torturous trip to, and aboard, Titanic.

Grudgingly, but slowly and surely, Titanic yields her secrets. . .

John P. Eaton,
Cold Spring, NY, USA,
March, 1966.

Acknowledgements

In the six years of intensive research for this project, many people have been involved and I would like to express my warmest thanks to all the major participants, namely:

* ROY STEMMAN, whose magazine inspired it;

* JACK PLEASANT, who provided the title,

* ESTHER, ARTHUR, MICHAEL and DOIRIN, who nagged me to keep on, when it seemed like a case of 'abandon all hope' of finding anything significant. I also gratefully acknowledge the assistance of the many experts and researchers; listed, more of less, in order of 'appearance':

* IN GREAT BRITAIN;

GEOFF WHITFIELD, STEVE RIGBY and BRIAN TICEHURST of the British Titanic Society for their extensive research, co operation and constant support; DAVID MONEY-COUTTS, who supplied details of his Latymer ancestors and the complex details surrounding the barony; JEAN WALMSLEY, MARTIN HEYS and other descendants of Andrew Latimer, chief steward, RMS Titanic; ANGELA BROOME, Royal Institution of Cornwall; RITA WARMINGTON, Cornwall Family History Society; REV. RODERICK THORP of Tiverton; GWEN ROUTLEDGE, of St Kew; KEN, JANETTE BUCKLEY and SHIRLEY KEEN, of Lanarth; LAURA WESTON, Public Relations Manager, National Maritime Museum, Greenwich; STAFF at Ravenswood School and at the Cornish Studies Library, County Records Office, Devon and Cornwall Constabulary; Reflections Coffee Shop, Newton-le-Willows;

CLERGY at various Lancashire and Cornish churches; PAUL CALLAN, journalist and broadcaster; BILLY BUTLER and WALLY SCOTT, late of BBC Radio Merseyside; but currently broadcasting on Radio City 1548am. DAVID ST JOHN THOMAS, author, publisher, expert on West Country railways; ANDREW SELBY, regression researcher.

* IN IRELAND

TOM WILLIAMS, who did so much of the early digging, then sustained his interest and friendship; ED COGHLAN, Irish Titanic Historical Society; EVERYONE connected with Cobh Heritage Centre; CANON SEAMUS BOLAND in Mayo; GERRY RYAN, RTE2; and most exciting of all JIMMY LENNON, whose magical appearance at the 11th hour, produced the final piece of the jigsaw.

* IN AMERICA

JOHN P. EATON and CHARLES A. HAAS, Titanic International Inc., New Jersey, for their continued help and frienship; ED KAMUDA, Titanic Historical Society, Indian Orchard, Ma., and his wife KAREN, for her kind review of my earlier Titanic book; BOB BRACKEN, New Jersey, for pointing me in the right direction for this one.

And finally, may I offer a special word of gratitude and lots of love to three very special friends, for their support and encouragement. They are JOY CIESLIK, of Wirral; SHARON and MICHAEL BOTT, formerly of London, and now of Banbury.

Introduction

This is a story about hypnotic regression.

Interest in regression has increased considerably during recent years. A search for the meaning of life has led many people to believe that regression provides what they're looking for; namely, evidence of rebirth.

For the benefit of readers who may not have encountered the phenomenon of regression, I should explain that it is the technique whereby people are induced into a very deep state of hypnosis and their memories directed back as far as those people are willing - or able - to go.

If there are no stumbling blocks on the way, the memories can go racing through the years to the participant's birth... and beyond. Stumbling blocks, however, frequently crop up and methods of removing them are fully explained elsewhere.[*1]

What is regression like from a personal point of view?

I can only describe it as a sequence of re-lived experiences of an earlier period of time as in moving picture flashbacks. In the pages that follow, I have recorded them more or less as they occured.

Writing this book has presented me with a very exciting challenge, mainly because of the remarkable body of material which has come into my hands and the exciting discoveries upon which I have stumbled: some of it, quite accidentally.

In the end, I'm not sure what conclusions to draw, or what hypotheses to present because much of what has happened defies rationalisation.

Are our minds capable of surviving bodily death? Naturally, I believe they are, and the evidence of the following pages seems to support my view.

Whether it can be attributed to reincarnation is up to the reader to decide. . .

Eight and a half decades have passed since the demise of the Royal Mail Steamer, Titanic; yet the lure of the ill-fated liner is as strong as ever. Along the south coast of Ireland, the few old folk whose memories stretch back that far say hers was 'a terrible beauty'. They recall how she lay at anchor beyond a place called Queenstown, which has since been renamed Cobh. And they tell of how, as the emigrants set off in their tenders to be transferred to the magnificent new steamer, the Angelus bell from a church on the hill pealed out across the water, calling the faithful to pray. 'Ring-a-bella-bay', the place is now called; and a wonderful view can be obtained of it by visiting what is generally acknowledged as the saddest shore in Ireland.

But the appreciation of the White Star liner which sank on her maiden voyage from Southampton to New York is not restricted to the elderly. Innumerable young and middle-aged people walk about this earth, inexplicably haunted by the story of that illfated voyage; intrigued by the life and death of the proud liner, and all who sailed in her. Titanic societies flourish the world over[*2] as whole new generations of enthusiasts are born. Schoolchildren and students increasingly choose the topic for serious study. Few of us alive today were around when the tragedy occured. That is irrelevant.

The story of the doomed vessel, though carved from Time itself, is timeless. . .

Titanic was a noble ship; the secrets she held to her bosom she took to her grave. Only now, in the wake of her discovery on the seabed, are they coming to light. Of the many stories surrounding the ship and her passengers, one relates to a young British heiress and a labourer who worked in her father's fields. At least, THAT was what we were given to understand during early regressions.

The hypnotherapist who conducted my regression to what I believe to be a previous life was Joe Keeton, who is also my husband. The individual, whose story emerged, proved to be a much more complex character than she appeared at the outset. It was not until more than five years into the research that we discovered a love triangle and attempted to unravel its mystery.

It was a story with as strong an Irish connection as Titanic herself.

To explain the significance of Titanic's Irish connection, we must step back into the final days of the 19th century.

In the aftermath of the Great Potato Famine, emigration to America seemed the only option for many impoverished young men and women. In search of a better life for themselves, thousands of Irish people were leaving their homeland. By the turn of the century, emigration from Ireland was at its height, with more and more young people booking passage for the New World on any vessel steaming across the Atlantic.

Those preparing to set forth on that sunny April morning in 1912 had not particularly asked to sail on RMS Titanic.

The 'queen of the ocean' was just one of the many vessels heading out in the right direction. Trawlers, cattle steamers or tramps would have done equally well. What did they care who built the new ship, how grand she was, or how many passengers she could take on board? The journey was but a means to an end.

In the counties of Mayo, Sligo, Galway, Clare, Limerick and Kerry, they made their arrangements. Most of the emigrants left with the blessing of their families, but there were also reports of family feuds, secret marriages and elopments.

Those preparing to leave their homeland trekked the many miles to Queenstown by foot, on the back of donkeys and mules and in assorted horse-drawn vehicles, glad of any form of transport to convey them across the ocean.

How utterly tragic then, that something as innocent as a coal strike should have effectively sealed the fate of so many. The strike resulted in several travellers having to be switched at the last minute to the doomed liner.

Aboard the Ship of Ships, they made plans for a future that was not to be. On that night of a thousand stars, the lives of our eloping couple ended in the icy waters of the North Atlantic: two of the 1,523 souls who perished. . .

Bereaved Irish families never ceased to pray for the repose of the souls of their loved ones. In Cork, Kerry, Galway, Mayo, Sligo, Longford, they remembered them at Masses and when chanting their rosaries.

One of the dead was a young man who had left his home in the Irish midlands with a mysterious lady companion, about whom virtually nothing was known.

When Titanic foundered, the couple were listed among those who were lost . .

For 73 years, the ship and her precious human cargo lay undisturbed on the ocean bed.

Then, in 1985, after decades of futile searching on the part of numerous teams of divers, the hulk of what had once been the world's most magnificent liner, was discovered.

In 1995, my own researches reached a significant milestone, when the path of the eloping Irishman's family crossed my own and a remarkable story began to unfold.

Is the story fact, fiction, or some sort of esoteric mix of the two?

THAT is up to the reader to decide. . .

NOTES, INTRODUCTION

*1. Keeton, Joe, with Simon Petherick: The Power of the Mind, Robert Hale (1988)

*2. The Titanic Historical Society and Titanic International are both American-based; the British Titanic Society, founded in 1986 with a handful of members, currently numbers almost a thousand: the Irish Titanic Historical Society (Dublin-based) and Ulster Titanic Society (Belfast) are both flourishing; thousands more enthusiasts live in Switzerland, Scandinavia, New Zealand and Australia.

PART ONE

Chapters 1 - 10

Introduction to regression

Chapter 1

Cheshire, England, Spring, 1990.

"Time has stopped.

"Like everything else in the universe, Time goes in circles. You have reached the top of that circle and you are now going back. You are drifting through time, further back through time... drifting, drifting. You're looking for a set of memories. They could be the memories of anyone, anywhere, any time; but that's what you're looking for: a set of memories.

"I don't want you to recall anything you have read, been told, or seen on television. Recall only the memories of something you yourself have experienced.

"Now relax... relax. Listen to my voice... keep drifting... You are going down a long, dark tunnel. All tunnels come out into daylight and as soon as that light starts filtering through, I want you to drift towards it.

"When you come out of the tunnel, you will see where you are... Can you see where you are?" The deep, rich voice pauses briefly. I know it is addressing me, but for some unfathomable reason, I am unable to reply. Verbally, that is: though I am certainly responding to the suggestions.

I feel as if I am in a dark, empty space where four of the five senses no longer exist. Or if they do, they're in a state of suspended animation. It is not an unpleasant state. On the contrary; it is very pleasant. I am more relaxed than I ever thought possible.

I can only describe it as a state of nothingness.

So the voice resumes its monotone, telling me to keep drifting...

"You're looking for memories; memories of events which have happened to you. They have actually happened to you, but they happened before you were born."

The voice is that of Joe Keeton, the internationally renowned regressive hypnotherapist, who is also my husband.

"You, Monica, have not yet been born.

"Keep drifting back; drifting, drifting until you see a light. Can you see a light....?"

At that point, my eyelids apparently begin to flicker, which provides the necessary clue to the observer, but I am hardly aware of the fact because, as far as I am concerned, something much more exciting is happening.

Pictures have begun to appear before me and, although I am still fully aware of the fact that I am sitting in a comfortable chair at home with my husband and a group of friends, I also feel as if I am on board some sort of rowing boat heading out to sea.

Drifting?

Not exactly. I am definitely going somewhere. But at this point my destination is irrelevant because it is the image of the boat itself and my fellow passengers that my attention is now focussed on. The boat is rickety and solidly packed with men and women in old-fashioned dresses. Some seem happy, others sad. A tall young man is about to strike up a tune on his bagpipes.

The fact that the image appears to be superimposed on that of my present day surroundings does not raise any questions in my normally enquiring mind.

At one and the same time I am watching the scene and am part of it. At this point, being a firm believer in reincarnation, I would like to say that I know this is the start of my longawaited journey into the past. But I don't know any such thing. The hypnotised and regressed mind doesn't work like that.

If such thoughts are flowing through then that mind is not sufficiently deep into the hypnotic state necessary for regression.

In this lovely, soporific state, all I want to do is shake hands with the person whose life has been recycled to manufacture the character that I am today.

"Bring out the memories," intones the rich brown voice which has taken on the extra quality of being able to probe right through to the epicentre of my subconscious "You are there... NOW!... " There's a brief pause, then I'm asked "Where are you... what can you see... what is your name...?"

The voice of my husband (who, of course was not my husband in that previous incarnation and whose voice, therefore, has suddenly become that of a stranger) comes through loud and clear. I shift my position slightly.

"What is your name?" he repeats.

"L...L..." I am struggling to get it out.

"Where are you?"

"I am HERE!" I hear myself announce, surprised at the need to be asked, for surely the questioner can see where I am. "On a boat... water... lots of people..." then suddenly, the words begin to flow. The memories, which began with a trickle, start flooding through me, with all the attendant emotion.

Looking out to sea, I realise the rowing boat is heading for a massive vessel anchored some way out.

"That ship... it is... it is... too BIG!"

"What ship?"

"Out THERE..." I point and still in my state of deep hypnosis, cry out: "It is too big. Too heavy for the water. It will sink. We will all be drowned..." I begin trembling.

"What is the ship called?"

I do not answer because, frankly, I do not know. And the question seems irrelevant. My main sensation is of fear and the nearer the crowded little boat approaches the huge ship, the more frightened I become. It is the sheer size of the ship that terrifies me.

"Drift off to sleep... off to sleep..." instructs the voice and almost instantaneously, the vision vanishes and I am back in that soft warm state of nothingness.

I am directed to let my memories move on to a happier time and, after a period of brief relaxation, guided back to my present persona, urged to recall everything I have seen and heard under regression, but to leave any pain and emotion behind.

"You are Monica again, back in 1990... five, four, three, two, one... WIDE AWAKE...."

Hey presto. I'm home and dry again...back in the here and now. Was what I have just experienced really a trip through time?

I have been regressed before, but only through events in my own life. This is my first attempt at journeying into earlier times. . .

In my waking state, after that attempt at pre birth regression, I recall that the only strong memories I have are of sitting on board a crowded boat sailing out towards a giant ship.

I know I was overcome by abject terror at the awesome size of the vessel, though thankfully out of regression and out of hypnosis, that fear has dissipated. Irritatingly, though, I still cannot name the ship, the port of embarkation, or even whether the L... with which in that other persona - I was struggling, was my first or second name... or even the name of the place where I might have lived.

Consciously, I find myself wondering is why I was travelling on a silly little boat. If I was about to make the journey of a lifetime (albeit someone else's) why was I not floating across the sky accompanied by a heavenly choir, in the words of the great William Wordsworth, 'trailing clouds of glory'?[*1] That sort of style would certainly be more in keeping with my personality.

Having recovered from the initial disappointment about my mode of transport, I wonder who this L... character was and why she and all those others were crammed like sardines into that uncomfortable little craft.

The concept of crossing the legendary River Styx doesn't - if one will pardon the expression - hold water; because this was no river. It was the sea. Of that much, I am convinced; even if everything else is hazy.

It is not unusual for first attempts at regression to produce these sort of vague images. Second and subsequent sessions bring out the details as memories of the person under hypnosis become increasingly clear.

If it is frustrating for me, it is equally so for my husband because, in all the years Joe Keeton has been practising as a hypnotherapist, this is the first time he has encountered anything connected with a ship which might well have been Titanic.

For me, it is exciting.

Is this where my abiding interest in the ill fated liner has its roots? Are memories of being lost on the ship the cause of my lifelong fear of still dark water, or is the regression a product of my imagination to explain that fear?

I cannot wait to have another try at regressing to the unknown character whose memories I appear to share. Apart from the fascination with Titanic, I'm a journalist, with all the attendant curiosity of my profession.

If there's a story here, I'll crack it. . .

NOTE, CHAPTER ONE

*1 Wordsworth, William: Ode, Intimations of Immortality.

Chapter 2

Why should anyone want to be regressed?

By the same token, why should anyone want to climb Mount Everest or swim the English Channel?

The answer is that it is probably a combination of curiosity, a sense of adventure, and excitement at what might lie in store.

Where the journey into pre-birth memories scores over that of the swimmer and the mountain climber is in its extra bonus: for, remarkable though it may seem, the journey of the mind can be shown to dispense with fears, phobias and mystery illnesses.

My own fear of water is not an isolated case. There are many documented cases of such problems having been found to have links with events experienced in previous memories: though in all honesty, I have to admit that Joe Keeton's case files show that MOST originate in traumas of THIS life.*[1]

Our minds are sometimes compared to computers because the information they give out is only as good as that which has been fed in and stored in the memory banks for recall whenever necessary. Provided the subject undergoing hypnosis is in a sufficiently deep state of relaxation, events of the past are not just remembered, but relived exactly as they happened at the time.

My original attempt at regression was to try and establish why I was so frightened of still black water (no other type bothered me, and travelling abroad by sea has never caused any problems).

Stumbling into (and even more dramatically, OUT OF) the Titanic was an added bonus; though to say it was beyond my wildest dreams would not be quite true.

Because dreams also figure strongly in this story. . .

The technique of age regression involves putting people into the deepest form of hypnosis and sending them back through their memories to relive past experiences, first in their own lives, then before birth and conception to-whatever memories are stored in the deepest recesses of the mind.

Over a period of 30 years, Joe Keeton has conducted several thousand regressions and has amassed an extensive collection of tape-recordings of conversations with what would seem to be people long dead.[*2]

In cases where trauma causing the problem cannot be traced to the person's own lifetime, it does seem that the fears and phobias are rooted much deeper in the memory and can only be reached by the operator's taking his subjects into the very deepest level of hypnosis, directing them right back to birth, then telling them that they are in times before they were born.

My own illogical fear of water could not be explained by anything in my present life and it was primarily to discover the cause and root it out, that I first requested regression. With luck, the origin of a recurrent nightmare would be discovered, too.

There are many offshoots from pre-life regression. Those of us who have been successfully regressed become more mature and can call upon more experiences than we would normally be able to.

Memory recall for one young nursing sister related to a woman who became very difficult before she (the woman) died, in her nineties. Upon arousal from hypnosis, the sister remarked that she would be considerably more sympathetic with her geriatric patients, now she had personal knowledge of senility.

We do not fully understand how the brain works, but we can interpret the primitive aspects of its functioning from our own findings, and Joe Keeton is quick to point out that HIS views are not necessarily those held by more orthodox thinkers. His personal belief is that because the subconscious is so powerful, it operates continuously and efficiently from the moment it is formed in the womb; though when exactly that is, he has no idea, nor does he attempt to define when consciousness itself begins.

Nor is he wholeheartedly sold on the idea of reincarnation. While he accepts that reincarnation certainly COULD be the answer, he likes to put forward other possibilities.*3

There is no lack of plausible explanations for past-life regressions. These might include fantasy, imagination, and cosmic memory (where disembodied thoughts can be picked out of the ether, as it were). Other possibilities: telepathy, genetically inherited memory, even the quantum theory of a parallel universe.*4 Take your pick. Joe Keeton's personal preference is for inherited memory.

Just as we inherit the colour of our eyes, the shape of our nose or teeth from our ancestors, isn't it feasible that we should also inherit their memories?

Well, yes, I suppose it is, but my own belief is still in reincarnation. If it was good enough for Pythagoras (with his Transmigration of Souls theory), it's good enough for me.

After all, nothing else in the universe is destroyed; so why should the human Life Force be the exception? Might this not be the ultimate form of energy conservation?

NOTES, CHAPTER TWO

*1 O'Hara, Monica, New Hope Through Hypnotherapy, Abacus (1980) pp 82 -100

*2 Moss, Peter with Joe Keeton, Encounters With the Past, Sidgwick and Jackson (1979)

*3 Keeton, Joe with Simon Petherick, The Power of the Mind, Robert Hale (1988) pp 35 - 77

*4 The quantum theory was originated by the German physicist, Max Planck in 1900. It postulates that, alongside our universe, there is an infinite number of parallel universes just as real as our own. Einstein's application of the quantum theory to light (1905) led to the theories of relativity. In 1918, Plank's quantum theory won him the Nobel Prize for Physics.

Chapter 3

Not all my recurrent dreams were nightmares and I suppose I should consider myself more fortunate than most in that I had five of them, all told.

While the watery one was certainly the most frightening, the other three had no associated emotions whatever. They were simply situations, in which I happened to be a part, and appeared to be totally disconnected.

In one, I was sitting in a black hansom cab behind two rather lovely horses. I knew I had alighted from a train before entering the cab. I also sensed that I was not alone and, judging by the heavy breathing and slow movement of the animals, that we were moving up a steep hill. No more.

The second dream had me strolling along a seaside promenade. I had no idea of the venue and it was irrelevant anyway. The most dominant aspect of that dream was the sight of several ladies and gentlemen strolling along the prom, sitting on benches, and queueing for refreshments at some sort of makeshift booth which was positioned on the road behind them.

The road ran parallel to the promenade and separated the masses of people (all in old fashioned clothes) from the hotels and shops. Between the promenade and the beach were white railings, then beautifully manicured lawns and gardens. It struck me as being a very Victorian, or possibly even Edwardian, sort of scene. The fourth recurrent dream had me still in the resort - wherever it was - still in the company of someone whose identity never became clear.

Only in this one, I was entering one of those seafront hotels. It had an archway coming out from its entrance, right to the edge of the pavement, rather like that of the Waldorf Astoria in New York.

The final dream appeared totally unconnected with any of the others. It was simply an image of a large white house, standing in its own grounds. A Georgia-type building, it was double fronted and surrounded by trees. I appeared to be observing it from the end of a long drive.

And that's it... apart from a very strange sensation I got every time I heard the name Latimer. Not only did it send goose pimples racing up and down my spine, but enigmatically, it conjured up pictures of a tall, distinguished looking man, with hair greying at the temples, gaunt cheeks and the sternest expression I have ever seen.

Were all these dreams and images in any way connected with each other, or had I been over-indulging in cheese at bedtime? Blessed with a fertile imagination, had I allowed it to go into overdrive while asleep?

Unable to fathom it out, I had long since stopped trying, so had the shock of my life when, after a series of regressions, all the strangely-shaped pieces of jigsaw started falling into place and the total picture began to emerge.

But I'm jumping ahead. . .

After that first regression, Joe and I mutually decided that a spot of further investigation might not go amiss. Another meeting with my alter-ego was called for.

This time, after easing me back gently into the character, he suggested I bring out the memories of when that curious character was a child,

"You are there again...." I was told. "Now go back... further back into the memories of whoever it was on that boat..drifting back again.... you are six years old.... where are you?"

"I am here!" came my response. I felt myself sitting on the grass in the shade of a very old tree. I was all alone.

"What is your name?"

"Lucie, Lucie Latymer.... my dadda's a baron..." I heard myself chant, and went on to tell my questioner about the unusual spelling of both my first and second names.

"Your dadda's a baron, is he.... what about your mummy?"

"My mummy's not here...." I dissolved into tears. "She fell in the pond. .." The tears were now flowing so copiously that, once more, I had to be brought out of regression, out of hypnosis and gently returned to the present.

But at least, my character now had a name. And a title.

During subsequent regressions to Lucie, sent back to her childhood, I could not emphasise strongly enough that MY father was the baron. The clipped speech tones and general aristocratic air appeared to confirm the observation.

Lucie's insistence could have been because, in her opinion, the man who actually became Baron Latymer had not been entitled to the honour: that it was HER father who should have been ennobled.

On the other hand, it could have been that, as an only child, she was a bit of a day dreamer and suffering from delusions of grandeur. Occasionally, she was heard to mutter something that sounded like 'earl' or 'earls'*[1] but pulled herself up sharply when she did so.

The third possibility was that her father really WAS Baron Latymer, or even that she was the daughter of an Earl: though there are strong arguments against either of these claims, as we shall see.

Lucie was no more forthcoming as a young adult. She was consistently snooty and refused to give any information about herself. Asked for personal details, she would respond simply along the lines of 'Have we been introduced?', 'Do I KNOW you?' and so on.

She positively refused to state her place of birth: repeating only her wild claims to have connections with a baron, an earl, or earls. Questioners half expected her claims of aristocratic connections to be upgraded to Royalty at any moment: though they never were.

On the rare occasions she deigned to answer any questions about her mode of transport and whether she was alone or in company, she refused to be specific, other than to state, with more than a hint of arrogance that she was with her 'retinue'.

While she never actually named Titanic as the ship on which she was sailing to America, the dates and all the circumstances of the regression made it impossible to be any other vessel. The extreme cold and the shivering which she - I - felt when regressed to the night of April 14/15, 1912 were VERY real.

Even now, as I think of it consciously, I can again feel that cold. My hands on the computer keyboard are suddenly frozen stiff (and I have to resort to self-hypnosis to warm them up again).

Under no circumstances would Lucie give her name as an adult. It was only when, once again, her memories were sped back to childhood that she volunteered the name of Lucie Latymer, insisting as always, that the Christian name was spelt with an 'ie', the surname with a 'y' and that she was the daughter of a baron.

The genuine, historical circumstances surrounding the barony of Latymer will be examined in a later chapter.

So, too, will the connection between the hansom cab, the bustling promenade, the hotel with the extended canopy... and, of course, the white house in the country.

Research proved long and difficult; but my journalistic background meant that I had access to people and places I might not otherwise have had. Even then, it was not all plain sailing (pardon the pun); because I was soon to discover that many of the leads I followed came to dead ends and what appeared to be hard evidence evaporated before me. No game of snakes and ladders was ever so infuriating. Nevertheless, I did manage to get there, in the end (which was more than poor Lucie did... in THAT life, anyway).

A minor point: although I felt sure that, when regressed to young womanhood, milady was with a mysterious male companion - because I could SENSE his presence in the hansom cab, standing outside the hotel and rowing out to sea - his name seldom crossed her lips.

When she did refer to him, it was by the pet name she herself had given him. It was not until much later that I found out the reason for her coyness.

The discovery was not made by me, but by an executive of the British Titanic Society, via a message on Teletext. That message also eventually pointed me in the direction of the big white house.

NOTE, CHAPTER THREE

*1 The significance of this claim remained obscure for a further five years. When it did come to light, it was not at all what anyone had expected!

Chapter 4

Lucie, in early childhood, was not very forthcoming; probably because her life was not terribly interesting. Questions were never answered directly; all she ever did was chant the same old sing-song: 'Lucie, Lucie Latymer... my dadda's a baron...'

Subsequent regressions to childhood produced the information that she was born shortly before Christmas; year unknown. Asked about her mother's fall in the pond, she managed to explain that the water was not very deep, but the poor lady fell on her head and the child apparently stood gazing at the inert figure for some time before calling for help. There was no way of knowing whether the injuries were fatal or not.

"Papa was very sad. He said I must keep away from water," I heard myself say.

Taken to a few years later Lucie, now apparently motherless, was to be found whingeing about her horrid governess, whom she named Miss Prim. In the persona of Lucie, my impression was that the newcomer was rather more than that; and I resented her bitterly.

Nothing important emerged from Lucie's adolescence, but around the age of 15, a new name emerged. It was that of 'Stennie'; whom she described as a youth who worked for Papa. Lucie confessed to being in the habit of watching him both from her bedroom window and from her favourite spot in the garden: sitting on an ivy-covered tree trunk, ostensibly working at some tapestry.

To the irritation of those questioning her, Lucie came through as being bored and boring.. She longed for the pleasures of the world, but Papa deprived her of them. He was so strict. He never smiled and hardly ever spoke, except to scold her.

Unable to communicate with her father, Lucie turned increasingly to the jobbing gardener who was, apparently, friendly and compassionate, being the only person who offered any solace when she was wracked with grief at the death of a pet dog.

Other than that, her days were spent listening to music, painting, reading and pursuing various forms of dainty handiwork, in keeping with other young ladies of her day. Lucie was clearly no intellectual and she had no friends outside those selected by Papa.

She persistently refused to provide a location for her home; other than to mention that it was situated in a lovely valley and contained a stream and many orchards and a railway station down by the front gates.

Asked if it was near the sea, she responded that people came from all over the country to enjoy the waters at a nearby harbour. She would not, or could not, provide an address.

All of this made research into my regression very difficult and the only reason my hypnotherapist husband pursued it was because of its possible connection with the Titanic.

The idea of looking for the railway station was dismissed for two reasons: one, that no-one knew in what part of the country Lucie was supposed to be living; two, Beeching's cuts of the 1960s would probably have removed it from contemporary maps.

The one way of establishing this connection was by pressing Lucie's fast-forward button to the night of the tragedy.

But, before that, something else had to be established. He needed to determine whether this was a genuine recollection of a past life, or a little story dreamed up (albeit subconsciously) by the writer within me. Was it something I had fabricated from information learned, and long since forgotten consciously, but had stored away subconsciously, for retrieval during hypnotic recall?

In other words, was it a case of cryptomnesia (which, literally translated from the Greek, means hidden memory)?

Back in the hypnotic state again, I was instructed:

"Go back through your own life, Monica, to the point where your interest was first aroused in Titanic..."

Obediently, my memories raced backwards, until they stopped at the age of nine, when I was reliving a scene in my parents' bedroom in the Irish town where we then lived. I was enthralled by the story my late mother was telling me about the lovely liner that was lost on its maiden voyage. She began to sing the Bethany version of Nearer My God To Thee; explaining that someone of her acquaintance had been lost on that dreadful night so long ago.

Once again, I heard her voice tell me about all those unfortunate people who died, and went straight to heaven from the bottom of the sea. 'Their bodies are on the ocean bed, but their souls are being wafted up to heaven,' she said.'[1] My mother, a devout Catholic, frequently remembered them in her prayers.

Still under hypnosis, I was then directed to go to any time in my own life when I had read or heard anything about Lucie Latymer, Stennie, or Miss Prim. None of those three names produced anything but a blank.

"The clock has stopped again... now it is running backwards... I want you to go further back... drifting, drifting, to times before you were born. Bring out all the memories of Lucie. You are fifteen years old. Bring out a happy time in the life of Lucie. Can you see where you are?"

A smile.

"Where are you, Lucie?"

"In the garden, with ... With..." another smile.

"Drift off to sleep."

I did so and was enveloped again in soft velvety blackness.

"Now come forward to the year 1912. It is 1912... the night of April 14." I began trembling, my teeth were chattering: I had never known such cold. My fingers were blue and I felt as if I would never be warm again. I could not stop shivering. "Where are you, Lucie?"

I could hear the question, but was unable to answer: it was as if my very tongue were in deep freeze. For some ridiculous reason, I seemed to be sitting on an old-fashioned deck chair on board ship. A tartan travel rug rested on my knee. I was alone, but felt as though I was waiting for someone to join me.

The voice coming through time did not disturb me then, or at any other time during regressions. I could not see where it was coming from; but it was irrelevant. At that particular moment, the cold was causing me more distress than anything else.

"Cold..." I managed, at length. "Bitterly cold...." my shivering became so violent that I was moved away from the scene and told to relax for a few moments, before being returned to the present.

After a refreshing cup of tea, it was time for the Big One. How would I feel about being regressed to the death of Lucie?

Okay, I said, knowing that if I chickened out now, I would never learn the fate of the poor little rich girl and the friend of whom her stern father undoubtedly disapproved. It would niggle away in my mind like a rotten, untreated tooth festering away in the jaw. Having come thus far, I HAD to carry on.

But first, I needed another cup of tea. Yes, I was stalling. I admit it. And, appreciating my need for a break, my considerate husband turned his attention to one of the other regressees in our group: a middle aged woman, whose alter-ego was known only as Gal.

The child of a hunter, she recounted that she lived with her father in a tiny mountain hut. No date or venue could be established because the child was young, and her life ended tragically one night when - having waited several days for her father to return - she succumbed to what we took to be hypothermia and starvation.

In her final moments, the child's mind conjured up images of warmth and sustenance. Asked where she was, she managed to whisper that she was sitting before a huge log fire, tucking into a bowl of rabbit stew. Then her head lolled to one side, and Gal was no more.

Right then, Lucie: prepare to meet your fate.

I settled back in the chair, was induced gently into hypnosis and guided back in the old, familiar way.

"It is halfway through the night of April 14/15, 1912. Bring out all the memories of that night. You are there... NOW!"

I certainly was. The shivering had intensified; because now it was a mixture of cold and fear. Several moments passed before I was able to speak. I was still on board ship; still out on the deck, but now walking, running, and in a state of utter confusion because of the general panic aboard.

The deck was on an angle and icy cold black water was rapidly approaching me. My blue dress was soaking wet and I had lost one of my pretty little shoes.

Strange how the mind works at times of crisis. I was fully aware that all the other passengers and crew were running AWAY from the threatening water, but I was running into it,

"Lost," I cried. "Lost..." I repeated, over and over again.

"You are lost?" came the questioning voice in my head. "Where are you Lucie?"

I was unable to explain that it was not I who was lost, but my shoe. It was down there, somewhere below me, its dainty little heel caught in the slat on the deck. I had to retrieve it. I simply had to. I could not possibly follow the other people, wearing only one shoe. Whatever would they think?

The freezing black water had now reached my knees, my thighs, my chest. Breathing was becoming increasingly difficult as my lungs filled with water. It was rising at a terrifying rate... reaching my neck, my mouth, my nose, until I was gasping for breath. It was horrendous. Just when I thought I could take no more, fate stepped in as I believe she frequently does on such occasions. At that very moment, I noticed what I can only describe as a beautiful fairy castle ahead. Tall, sparkling like crystal, it beckoned to me. My love was already there: waiting for me.

I moved forward, lost my footing and was swallowed up by the sea. Lucie was no more.

Was it The Iceberg I had seen in those final moments of Lucie's life? Or was it, like Gal, something conjured up to make the passing easier?

NOTE, CHAPTER FOUR

*1 Sometime in the late 1920's or early 1930's, my mother - as a young girl - travelled from Liverpool to New York on the (first) ss Mauretania. At the helm was Captain Arthur Rostron, who had captained the ss Carpatia, the ship which rescued many of Titanic's survivors. She told me that during the voyage Captain Rostron (understandably regarded as a hero by his contemporaries) spoke emotionally about the tragedy, and about the hymn which had subsequently become an integral part of Titanic's story.

Chapter 5

During the course of the next year or so, I was regressed to the character of Lucie on several occasions: always in the company of several witnesses: to whom my husband frequently handed over the questioning and the research.

Geoff Whitfield, Honorary Secretary of the British Titanic Society, has spent many years delving into the real lives of the ship's passengers (both lost and saved). He has devoted every spare moment of his time to building his impressive portfolio. All the names, addresses, ages and personal details are filed away in his Liverpool home and, whenever a Titanic story breaks, newspaper reporters the world over seek his comments.

Although Geoff was able to state at the outset that no one named Lucie Latymer was to be found on any of the passenger lists (first class, second class, or steerage), several were travelling under assumed names. In the circumstances, he concluded, it seemed highly likely that if Lucie were on board, she would be travelling incognito.

Whether the unfortunate girl ever existed or not, all I could say at that stage was that the effects of those first attempts at pre-birth regression and the scenes being acted out in my subconscious mind, including the confrontation with death, proved wholly beneficial. Not only did they remove my irrational fear of water, but they made some sort of sense of the images which had been revolving in my brain for so long.

Now that we had managed to pinpoint them, they began to filter spontaneously through to my conscious: in other words, manifesting themselves when I was NOT under hypnosis. Into the forefront of my mind tumbled a kaleidoscope of pictures - or far distant memories, if that is what they were.

The way they entered my head was as random as any other group of memories but, for the sake of order, I shall present them in sequence, as I suspected they might have related to Titanic.

In the first, there I was again sitting alongside a mysterious companion in the back of a black, horse-drawn hackney cab, behind two magnificent looking horses. Sometimes the image was accompanied by memories of the warm, pungent smell one invariably associates with the animals.

Am I unique in finding that horsey smell so overwhelmingly nostalgic? Or does it evoke a host of memories in other people, too? Every time it hits my nostrils, I am transported straight back to that short journey up a hill, in anticipation of something exciting. It is as if someone had pressed the fast rewind button in my mind.

In those early days after the first few regressions, images of the seaside resort were also dominant, and there I continued to find myself and my mystery man surrounded by the multitudes.

The more frequently the image manifested itself, the more details it produced: particularly in relation to what all those other people were wearing. The women were in long dresses and the men in wing collared shirts. Some were sitting on benches, others standing close by, chatting. All appeared to be watching and waiting for something.

Recollections were clear, too, of a large white Georgian type manor house standing in several acres of ground; and that too, became clearer as time went by.

I could also visualise a magnificent staircase sweeping down to what looked like a huge hallway: a pair of very ornate lifts continuously transporting smartly dressed couples and fat, elderly ladies from one floor to the other. I use the word 'floor' rather than 'deck', because when these impressions first came through, I thought they might have been part of the big white house for which I constantly searched.

It was not until they had manifested themselves to me several times, that I began to feel the lifts were not in architectural keeping with the house: they were more suited to the style of an hotel or a large, ocean going liner.

As the months passed, the most distinct (conscious) memory of all was of being on some form of transport which was so big, so beautiful and so important that it was literally, the talk of the town: aha, but WHICH town? That was the sixty four thousand dollar question. It was absolutely intriguing because of the way that I actually felt important by association.

This might sound totally daft but, even today, that feeling hits me whenever I am sitting on a bus or train filled to overflowing. What sparks off the memory and its associated urge to wave is seeing crowds of people standing at a bus stop or on a station platform, watching my transport pass by.

No, I am not old enough to have travelled on the Titanic myself, I can only assume that my alter ego felt the urge to wave at onlookers watching the great liner move past them as they waved their farewells, from the shore: or wherever.

(It wasn't until much later that I discovered the shore was too far away for wellwishers to be seen; the only onlookers within view would have been those aboard the tender returning to dry land).

Not surprisingly, the strongest memory is that of walking along a slanting promenade in the opposite direction to everyone else; of catching a pretty little Louis heel in a wooden slat and tugging at it so desperately and for so long that I missed the last boat to safety. (I still love pretty shoes, though not to the extent that I would give up my life for one of them. A dog, yes. A shoe, no!)

Another far memory is of stepping into the water and 'walking' towards a tall structure. I fear Lucie must have been somewhat intellectually impaired. Why else would she have walked INTO the water, towards what she considered to be a fairy castle and the brilliant lights surrounding it?

All right, so she was probably attracted by its beauty and the urge to see who lived in it. But surely, she should have known that nobody could live in the middle of the North Atlantic, and that she would have been better off trying to board a lifeboat, like everybody else?

What an impression it must have made on her, though. Today, I have only to see a picture of The Iceberg and that fancy castle invariably superimposes itself on the printed image. Did I - or the unfortunate Lucie, whose memories I seem to share - really walk into the water towards the icy structure, with its rays of light beaming out from every window? And, if so, was it because the light of her life (so to speak) had gone on ahead and was beckoning to her from one of those bright windows?

If there are those who believe that it was because my mother told me about Titanic in childhood that I invented the whole episode to justify my irrational fear of water, let me raise a question.

Explain, please, why I should choose a resort in which I was not, at the time of those 1990/1991 regressions, familiar: though I did in fact subsequently visit the place, and very revealing it proved too (as will also be explained in a later chapter). How could I know all the historical details relating to the day Titanic sailed in to collect her final group of passengers from the place now known as Heartbreak Pier.

More curious still, however did the information about the barony of Latymer get into my head?

Could the character to whom I regressed have been one of my ancestors? Possibly, but if that were so, by what means could she have passed on the memory of her death?

As birds inherit the ability to fly and fish to swim, so too may the human metabolism contain a nucleus of genetic memories which, when tapped, are capable of yielding information hitherto unknown.

It is a fact that various latent abilities can be activated and dormant cells awakened under hypnosis, so is it not possible for long forgotten memories passed down a family line to be recalled during regressive hypnosis, or in lucid dreaming?

Might that not be how events of the past affect one's present day thoughts and deeds? It is possible, of course. But, as already pointed out, against that theory is the concept of genetically passing on the memories of one's own death and there we have a concept which seems to defy logic.

Indeed they ALL appear to defy logic apart from our old favourite: reincarnation. For my money, it is the most popular theory to explain regression and, with it, the notion of past incidences affecting present behaviour. It is certainly a most satisfactory means of explaining away those niggling phobias.

For many centuries, the Christian religions have been based on the assumption that when one departs this life, some mighty power decides on either eternal salvation, enjoying the 'glory of God', or eternal damnation, being deprived of it.

The tenets of the Christian church have been founded on such teachings which, although probably originally intended to be symbolic, have been taken literally by a vast majority of people in the past. Whereas most religions hold the view that there is some sort of life after death, it is the nature of that life that creates the stumbling block and gives rise to so many superstitious beliefs.

The basic tenet of all science is that no energy can be destroyed. If the Life Force which is contained in the human framework is a form of energy - which it definitely appears to be, since thought seems to produce electrical impulses - then there is no reason why there should be an exception in this particular instance. The Life Force too should be indestructible, and available for re use time and time again.

Reincarnation, or re use of that force, or spirit, or whatever other name we give it, seems to offer one explanation for the concept of regression, particularly in relation to the idea of retaining certain attributes, habits and symptoms.

The essential essence of our being may be eternal, indestructable and transmittable but to refer, as Pythagoras did, to its transmigration, gives the notion vaguely religious undertones which it does not necessarilly possess.

Ian Currie is a Canadian author and thanatologist (someone who specialises in the scientific study of death and its associated phenomena). He has written and lectured extensively on the after-life. His contention is that people can, and do, survive physical death.

When I interviewed him during a lecture tour to promote one of his books[*1] he spoke enthusiastically of his findings in relation to hauntings, deathbed visions, mediumistic communications and, of course, reincarnation claims: quoting Voltaire's observation 'Being born twice is no more remarkable than being born once.'

But enough of the philosophising: over to Lucie, for a potted biography of her relatively short life.

NOTE, CHAPTER FIVE

*1 Currie, Ian, You Cannot Die, Hamlyn (1988).

Chapter 6

Lucie appears to have been born some time in the early 1890s. The difficulty in pinning her down was because, when pressed for answers, she simply turned up her 'aristocratic' nose and responded sniffily that her age was no-one's business but her own.

If she is to be believed, her early childhood was one of happy, sun-dappled, days when nothing much happened other than a couple of house moves, the details of which could not be extracted from her. She was most unhelpful in providing information about any of her places of residence. The only impression provided was one of having grown up into a solitary sort of child, who grew up to be a bored, and therefore highly fanciful, teenager. When the virile labourer on her father's estate began making advances, Lucie's response is hardly surprising.

Questions about the date - even had she known it - would not have been appropriate when she was to be found as a small child, confused and bewildered, gazing at the inert body of her mother in the pond. At the age of 15, when she was again in the garden, only now in the company of the jobbing gardener, the date would have been the last thought in her head. His name was never properly established, because she only ever referred to him as 'Stennie'. All I can say, retrospectively, is that the period in which she lived felt like the early days of this century; and my recollections of where she spent most of her life were of a very grand country house.

A mansion with stables, it stood in several acres of ground, on an estate that was miles away from anywhere.

In the deeper recesses of my memory, I can still hear (and smell) those steam trains chugging into and out of the little railway station at the end of the drive.

Papa, whether a baron or a gentleman farmer, was certainly lord of the manor: wealthy, authoritative, aloof and autocratic. His gracious home had a library, music room, spacious drawing room, as well as a wine cellar below the kitchen and peacocks in the garden. The house was filled with priceless heirlooms, paintings, antiques, silverware, ceramics, fine china and porcelain.

In such an environment, most young ladies would have been happy: but not Lucie. It was all too repressive for her taste. Because her father insisted on putting distance between himself and his neighbours, Lucie's loneliness increased with every passing year. She spent hours of solitude in the garden, with only her pet dog, Brindley, for company.

Papa was utterably unapproachable. Mama, having been missing virtually throughout her formative years, never reappeared; which seems to suggest that the accident witnessed by the child had indeed proved fatal. Her only light relief came during her clandestine meetings with the ever affectionate Stennie.

We gathered that her young man was of gypsy stock. (Shades of Lady Chatterley? Definitely not: I had never read the story). He was an absolute knockout, with black, curly hair, deep brown eyes, and bronze, earth crusted skin.

He spoke in an accent that was more colourful than anything Lucie had ever heard among people living in the village down the road, or even in her previous place of residence. Stennie, questioned by Lucie about his speech, told her it was because, like herself, he had not been born in this part of the country, and had travelled far and wide before coming to work for His Lordship.

Having gained each other's trust, the pair pursued their relationship in secret places varying from the orchard, to a secluded corner of the walled garden, the huge old greenhouse and the cosy little potting shed.

Their meetings were not even for sexual satisfaction. Lucie was too prim - too unsophisticated - for that; and I suppose the youth too conscious of his fate if he did over-step the mark.

The inevitable happened.

Discovery of what was going on under his patrician nose sent Papa white with rage. He was, he stormed, at a loss to understand what had made a well brought up young lady of her class behave with such a lack of decorum. However much the girl protested her innocence, he refused to give her the benefit of his doubt. Surely, she realised the chap was a scoundrel and a fortune hunter.

It was hopeless.

Lucie, in a moment of sheer bravado, announced that if Papa could not accept the man who meant so much to her, then he could say goodbye to his daughter, too.

Predictably, she was sent to her room. Equally predictably, she escaped... into the earth bronzed arms of the labourer.

Their meeting took place at the end of the drive, in the very shadow of the darkened railway station, which was closed for the night.

Her small valise contained a change of clothing, some undergarments, a few coins and trinkets from the treasure chest at the bottom of her bed. Around her neck, she wore a locket containing pictures of Mama and her beloved dog Brindley, both of whose passing she still mourned.

She had left no note for Papa, no fond farewell. She did not care whether she ever saw him or her nasty governess again. It gratified her greatly to reflect that by morning, on discovering her bed had not been slept in, and she was nowhere to be found, Papa would be like a raging bull. But, by then, the pair of them would be miles away. Shivering from a mixture of apprehension and excitement, the runaway took one last, lingering look at her home. Then she left it forever.

Thrilled at having escaped her place of incarceration, Lucie turned to Stennie. The man for whom she had given up everything whisked her away on the back of a stolen horse. He had relatives in the New World and that's where they would go.

"What?" she trilled. "Tonight...?" . . .

"Where are you, Lucie... what are you doing...?" the question was in her head only. She had heard it a few times before, but it never bothered her: not like it might had it been the voice of Papa.

Lucie was not saying where she was or what she was doing. Why should she? How could she be sure The Voice would not report back to Papa.

Not that he would have much success in catching her, for it was a long time since she had left home and many hundreds of miles now separated them. The journey for Lucie and her escort had included travels over land and sea. Such a lot had happened since the night she had run away.

Wouldn't Papa be gratified to know how dreadfully upsidedown her world had been turned,before righting itself, as if by a miracle, at the last minute? *[1]

She wasn't prepared to take chances, though. Even thinking about the affairs of her heart made her go goose-pimply. She switched her thoughts to more pleasurable matters... like her future with the heavenly, adoreable man whose hand she clasped as they sat side-by-side on a bench.

Just three days to go. Three days and they would be on the high seas, heading for an exciting new home of their own.

"Where are you, Lucie?" repeated The Voice. "Can you hear me?"

She nodded her head to show that of course she could hear. Did The Voice think she was deaf, or something? Whyever should she answer, anyway? She had no intention of telling it about her private life and The Voice had no business asking. It was rude to be so nosey.

"Drift off to sleep... off to sleep..." Yes, she did need that sleep. The journey here had been so very tiresome. Even he, sitting alongside her, was feeling the need to snooze. "Off to sleep, Lucie..."

In the warm, April sunshine, she felt herself nodding off, dozing, dreaming of her enchanted life ahead. She awoke feeling delightfully refreshed.

Life was good: better than she had ever known it. Her companion was the most wonderful person in the world and they were both wildly excited about the imminent arrival of the big ship.

There had been a bit of a mix-up over the tickets. The ship they were to sail on was not the one it was supposed to be, but then were she and her companion the PEOPLE they were supposed to be?

She was not the bored young lady whose spirit Papa had tried to crush. He, too, was different, but none of that mattered as long as they stayed together and continued to put hundreds of miles between themselves and Papa.

She glanced around her; sighing as she took in views of the town from various angles and reflected on the prettiness of the place. Lucie heard that there had been a Royal visit shortly before Her (late) Majesty's death and that the old Queen had loved the place so much the town's dignitaries had renamed it, in her honour. No wonder the Queen had been so impressed. The Royal lady would probably have made the most of the beautiful beachy walks, sandy coves and winding, hilly roads.

Just like herself, mused Lucie.

Local people kept offering the hand of friendship and, although her companion enjoyed a chat and a drink with the menfolk, she chose to keep her distance. Never at ease mingling with others, she was uncomfortable in the company of strangers. What if her tongue slipped?

She gazed out across the water to where their ship would arrive on Thursday morning and depart on the noonday tide. The papers were in order: safely tucked away in her hero's pocket.

Lucie's favourite blue dress had been washed, in preparation for the journey. It was a pity their plans to marry had not been successful. For appearance sake, they would travel as brother and sister, but would be man and wife within days of setting foot in New York

"Oh darling... unless it's possible for us to be married on board ship?" she suggested. "D'you think perhaps it might be?"

In response, he just gave her one of those devastating smiles that made his eyes twinkle and his whole, lovely, face light up. They embraced again.

Brother and sister indeed. How very amusing. They did not even remotely resemble each other. He was so dark and she so fair... not to mention the very obvious speech difference. That was another reason for letting him do all the talking.

She glanced again at the names on the tickets: Dennis and Mary Lennon. Papa would never find her now: if, indeed, he even WANTED to, which she doubted. Should she be a dutiful daughter and write him a short letter on arrival in New York?

"Come forward to April 11, 1912, Lucie. It is approaching mid-day on Thursday, April 11, 1912.....Where are you?"

It didn't matter any more. Lucie could answer The Voice now that she was on her way. She and her love were nearing the front of the queue moving forward along the ricketty jetty towards the tender.

She would be glad when they were aboard the big ship, though why it couldn't come in to them, instead of making them travel all that way out from the shore, she failed to understand. Funny little boats laden with souvenirs, lace and mailbags were preparing to sail out across the water alongside them.

They were on board the tender, now; moving slowly forward. The bells of a church on the hill behind them, pealing out solemnly for so long, stopped as the clock struck twelve.

Some of her fellow passengers crossed themselves and prayed aloud, together. 'Dennie', as she chose to call her companion, joined in. Lucie watched and listened; bemused. No, no. She must be careful. She wasn't Lucie any more. She was Mary, now. Mary Lennon, if anyone asked.

Except The Voice. No-one else could hear that, so she allowed it to continue calling her Lucie. The Voice knew her before she came here, none of these people did. There was nothing to connect Lucie with Mary, which was how she wanted it. To The Voice, she was an English lady... Lucie Latymer. To the authorities and everyone making this journey, she was Mary Lennon, who was Irish. They were two different people.

In order to keep up the pretence of being no different from the others, she shut her eyes and quietly intoned a prayer of her own; then, having watched her travelling companions make the Sign of the Cross, she perfected the technique and watched her 'brother' nod his approval.

In the past few days she had discovered how much religion meant to these people. They went to church every morning and prayed every time the bells tolled. They were constantly invoking the name of the Lord, the Virgin Mary and saints Lucie had never heard of.

How very different they were from Papa and herself, who had only ever graced the parish church on high days and holy days: and then simply to set an example to the cap doffing yokels of the village. Papa. Hmph!

The Voice repeated its question.

"Where are you, Lucie.. ?"

Her gaze took in the scene of hustle and bustle, but she chose not to reply. Prayers over, a tall thin man sitting opposite her, tuned up his pipes and began playing a mournful dirge. The other passengers called the pipes 'ill', or something similar - and the sound of them certainly made Lucie feel ill. It was so awful.

"You are not alone, are you, Lucie?" The Voice went on. She shook her head. "Who are you with?"

Her eyes panned around the boat, her gaze resting briefly on her amazingly handsome partner, before taking in a general view of the shabbily-dressed men and women still chanting their prayers. Domestic servants, they would be. To The Voice, she responded imperiously (and not without an element of mischief) "My retinue... I am with my retinue."

Poor Stennie, Dennie, or whoever he was. How did he put up with her? He must have been a very tolerant young man.

One wonders if he stopped to think at all about what he was letting himself in for.

NOTE, CHAPTER SIX

*1 If the reader is confused, I apologise, but it merely reflects the confusion researchers encountered in attempting to unravel the tangled mess. Who exactly WAS Lucie's partner? The task of identifying him took almost as long as attempts to find the lady herself. Five years' examination of yellowing documents eventually produced results. Bear with me... all will be revealed in later chapters.

Chapter 7

The mood on board the tender was mixed. Some of the men and women were weeping because they were leaving their little cottage homes and farmhouses not from choice, but from necessity. They-like our eloping couple - believed their only hope of prospering was by emigrating to the land of opportunity.

Lucie suspected that among their fellow passengers, there were others who were in the same position as Dennie and herself; the look in their eyes, and their unwillingness to chat to anyone else gave them away.

She turned her glance from them, back towards the shore, and drew her love's attention to the groups of white-washed houses dotted about the mountainside. In the mid-day sun, their gables and frontages gleamed against a background of greenery.

Lucie was reminded nostalgically of a cake Mama had baked for Christmas one year when she was very young. Shaped like a little house, it was covered in white icing sugar, and its roof 'thatched' with flakes of delicious chocolate. The door and windows were also made of chocolate; piped into shape from a paper funnel.

Mama was so very clever. Lucie missed her greatly and she felt sure that Mama would not have disapproved of her wonderful companion. Poor, dear Mama. Why did she have to trip and fall in the pond? If Papa had had it filled in before she did, the tragic accident would never have happened. Her death was Papa's fault. Everything was Papa's fault.

Did he ever love Mama, she wondered absently as she watched the white surf breaking against the shoreline.

The shapes of the little houses were becoming increasingly unclear as the shore began to fade from view. The paddlers, chugging alongside, laden with luggage and sacks of mail, were funny looking vessels. Lucie wondered if it would be more comfortable aboard one of those than this horrid, overcrowded tender with at least a hundred other people all squashed in together. She knew now what sardines would feel like in a tin if they were alive; which, fortunately, they were not. What a silly thought.

The man she must now think of as her brother caught her smile, reached out to hold her hand and smiled back. Her heart missed a beat. He was so handsome, and she loved him so much. 'Mary Lennon' couldn't wait to get to New York and start their new life together.

She understood that this was to be the big liner's last port of call before setting out onto the high seas and then it would be, as the others kept saying, 'full steam ahead' to America. These big ships could travel much faster than those old ones she used to watch when she managed to sneak out of her home and down to the harbour.

Now that they were nearing the huge liner, she could feel her whole body tingling. The twinge of apprehension she had felt before leaving home to begin her epic journey began to manifest itself again. Was she being foolhardy in expecting Dennie to spend the rest of his life with her? Were they doing the right thing in leaving everything behind?

It was such an ENORMOUS ship, standing there on top of the water that Lucie was not the only person overwhelmed by its size.

Many of the women voiced their fears aloud.

They were alongside now, ready to step on board.

"Where are you, Lucie? What are you doing?"

Oh botheration. Not The Voice again.

Well she certainly wasn't going to answer it when she needed all her attention to clamber up those slippery steps. This time, it did not repeat the question, and it left her alone until she was safely on board. Then she heard it again.

"Where are you, Lucie? Can you see where you are?"

"Of course!" she snapped back.

"Where are you?"

"I am here. On the big ship."

"Are you alone?"

"No..." she responded, irritated at the way the crowds were pushing and jostling against her. "I am still with my retinue."

Most of the men and women who had boarded with her appeared to have shaken off their anxiety and their menfolk were positively excited at the thought of what might lie ahead. Everyone wanted to see their rooms - or cabins, as they were called - and to look over the ship itself.

As the engines started up and the great vessel began to move, Lucie stood on deck hand-in-hand with her love. They stayed in that position as the ship sailed slowly along the coast, with the captain acknowledging the sirens and whistles of every passing ship. Then something horrible happened. Officials separated Dennie and herself. A uniformed steward explained that only married couples were allowed to stay together.

How careless of them. Why hadn't they pretended to be man and wife, instead of brother and sister? Neither had anticipated this. The uniformed man explained that single men and women were to be accommodated in different sections of the ship. Lucie explained in no uncertain terms that she was not a woman, but a lady. Despite herself, her demeanor was such that it always commanded attention.

The steward, hearing her manner of speech and noticing her expensive clothes and the gold locket hanging around her neck, actually apologised, and led her away from this meeting place and upstairs to the First Class section.

In all the chaos, he did not think to ask for her ticket.

The sight greeting her when she entered the First Class section made her gasp. It was so LUXURIOUS. No wonder the ladies and gentlemen were full of admiration as they gazed at the grand staircase. The hand rails had turned yellow gold from the sunlight streaming in though the wrought iron and glass dome directly above.

The sun was also beaming in on the polished oak walls and the gilt balustrades. Those of the puffed-up elderly ladies and their escorts who were not strolling up and down the magnificent stairs, were standing in front of the very ornate doors of the two matching lifts.

Lucie's breath was almost taken away as she gazed up at the beautiful panel on the landing, with its clock, surrounded by two figures symbolising Honour and Glory, crowning Time. But her joy was short-lived.

A white-gloved hand on her shoulder made her turn to face another steward, and this one WAS asking to see her ticket. She showed it to him, smiled sweetly and said she trusted everything was in order.

It most certainly was not, his gruff voice told her. She had no right to be here. Hers was a third class ticket, he growled, and ordered her straight back to where she belonged: in steerage.

His uniform might have been that of an officer, but he was no gentleman. He was a most uncouth man. Lucie objected strongly to the way she was being manhandled, but it made no difference.

She was ordered away from this beautiful place immediately, and back downstairs to where the awful man said she would have to stay for the rest of the journey.

Where was Dennie? Her dear, sweet Dennie? He had been ushered away to the other end of the ship before she had even had a change to say goodbye. Had he been shepherded, like herself, into this lower and infinitely less pleasant section of the ship where everything compared most unfavourably with the sumptuous first class compartments?

Oh Dennie, Dennie darling... where ARE you?

If she had never prayed in her life, she prayed now. Dear God, find him for me, PLEASE.

They should never have been separated. Where was he? Come along, God, please say where he is. Prayers did not come naturally to Lucie; God was a remote figure, with whom she had never been familiar.

She was not at all sure that she even BELIEVED in Him; though she thought perhaps this was not the place to make her opinions known; not with so many religious fanatics around. Anyway, as He did not seem very keen to do anything for her, she decided to go off in search of Dennie herself.

She crept stealthily along a corridor and peeped inside the open door of a cabin. The nasty, grey-haired woman inside took one look at her and shut the door in her face. Ignorant fool.

The stewardess who witnessed the incident was rather more sympathetic and asked Lucie who she was looking for. She explained that she was searching for her brother, Dennis Lennon. On describing him to the stewardess, she was told to go down to the end of the corridor where several of the men could be found in the smoking room.

The stewardess obviously did not know Dennie, or she would realise that he would never be in such a place, because he did not smoke. Had she tried the dining saloon and the general lounge, then? She had tried everywhere, she told the girl. Without success. Her 'brother' was nowhere to be found. The girl promised she would keep a lookout for him, and Lucie thanked her as she wandered off, to continue with her duties.

Lucie was not normally one for showing her emotions, but alone again, her eyes began to sting and soon hot tears were rolling down her cheeks. She was utterly desolate.

Apart from wanting to nestle in Dennie's arms again and affirm her love for him, she thought it would be rather a novel idea to sneak him upstairs and show him the beautiful rooms in First Class.

How lovely if they could take tea in the cafe Parisien, or the verandah cafe, into both of which she had peeped before that horrid man had pushed her away. She had not seen the dining room, but had overhead a fat and feathered matron describe its splendour.

Dreams, dreams.

She knew full well she would not be allowed up there again: with or without Dennie. How lovely it would have been, though, to be accommodated with her love in one of the first class staterooms, instead of having to settle for these public rooms which had no privacy whatever.

Everything down here was horrid. Servants' quarters they were. Worse. Servants would be dismissed if they behaved like this: being noisy, and SICK, if you please. There really was no excuse for that, because the sea was perfectly calm. Had they no self-control?

And those ghastly children: crying and shouting at each other like little savages. The fact that she was missing Dennie so much was making Lucie irritable and despondent.

They had only been sailing a short time when one silly woman, leaning over the deck and praying with her beads, let them drop into the shimmering water below and, as she watched them float away, began wailing that it was an omen. Her rosary was lost, now she too would be lost, she insisted. The ship was going to sink. That sort of hysteria really annoyed Lucie. These people were so superstitious.

No amount of consoling or placating would quieten the sobbing woman. Lucie gave her a filthy look, so there was no doubt in anyone's mind how SHE felt.

She strutted off in disgust. In the place they called the lounge, she ordered a refreshing cup of tea.

"Can you see where you are, Lucie?" Oh not The Voice again.

She could, but she was not very impressed at the sight. And she told The Voice as much.

"Where are you?" it asked, as it frequently did.

"I am here... taking tea..."

"Afternoon tea, is it?"

"Yes," she smiled sardonically. Afternoon tea at Lucie's home consisted of cucumber sandwiches and cream cakes with jam. Served on a silver tray, of course.

Sometimes she would have toasted scones, cream crackers and cook's special: a crumbly lemon flavoured madeira cake, and there was always fresh fruit in season. She was used to nothing less. Had she not seen the splendid First Class section of this ship she might not have considered this part so inferior, but she had, and she did, and she made her views known, in no uncertain terms.

"Have you met any of the other passengers yet, Lucie?"

What a silly question. Of course she had met them, but they were not the sort of people with whom she would be likely to associate.

"What are their names?" asked The Voice.

"How should I know?" she snapped.

"Have you not been introduced?"

"I do not wish to be introduced," she stated imperiously.

"Why is that, Lucie?"

Gracious! How could she even begin to answer such a question? Was it not obvious?

She strolled out on deck.

The wailing woman and her miserable friends had gone, thank goodness, so she found herself a steamer chair and sat for a while in solitude.

"Where are you now, Lucie?"

"I am on deck."

"What is the weather like?"

"It is a pleasant afternoon," she responded formally.

"Are you alone?"

"At the moment, yes."

"Not with your retinue?" teased The Voice.

But Lucie was in no mood for jesting.

"I am quite alone," she said sadly, her thoughts only on Dennie.

"Relax, Lucie...drift off to sleep...off to sleep...Now come forward to Friday. It is Friday, April 12, 1912. Where are you?"

She was still on board ship: would be for several more days.

She smiled. She was with Dennie, so was happy again. They kissed passionately, oblivious to anyone who might have seen, and suspected the truth.

"Where are you, Lucie?" repeated The Voice.

"I am with Stennie," she told it, because mention of Dennie would have been most unwise. She no longer cared who knew she was in love. Safe in his company on this fast-moving ship to America, she did not care if the whole world knew of their plans.

Papa could do nothing to stop them now. No-one could. Their future together was assured.

Chapter 8

Saturday, April 13, dawned bright and clear; although out in the middle of the Atlantic, it had turned cold. Cloaks, coats and shawls were thrown over the shoulders of those passengers who enjoyed spending their time on deck.

Lucie arose early, breakfasted and spent the rest of her happy, happy day with Dennie. Fat matrons, surrounded by hoardes of children, smiled benevolently at the closeness of the Lennon siblings. How good it was to see a brother and sister so fond of each other, one was heard to remark. Ha, if only they knew.

She and Dennie spent much time on the forward open deck space, to see where the ship was heading. Land was not yet in sight, but it would be in a few days time. And then... freedom.

After lunch, they sauntered, hand in hand into the general room where a piano had been installed. Having heard the sounds of Ragtime floating down from the First Class section, Lucie tried tinkling the ivories herself. But she had not been taught that type of music, so instead treated her appreciative audience to snatches of Mozart and Chopin. No one seemed to notice when she struck wrong notes and it was bliss not to be rapped on the knuckles as she would have been at home.

When she had finished playing, the audience clapped and Lucie did a curtsey. They clapped again at that, and asked her to play some more. Lucie felt very important. It was the first time in her life anyone had ever applauded her for anything. She had never expected these people to appreciate classical music. Life was full of surprises.

Perhaps they were not such a bad lot, after all.

Encouraged and energised by the audience's reaction to Lucie's music-making, Dennie crooned a love song and they clapped even louder; now stamping their feet and shouting for more.

Having exhausted their repertoires, the two took themselves out into the fresh air again; found a couple of steamer chairs and sat down side by side, discussing their plans. When the sea breezes turned chilly, they returned-indoors and enjoyed a game of dominoes. After that, Lucie made extensive entries in her diary and Dennie played patience with the grubby pack of cards he kept permanently in his pocket.

They watched the more energetic travellers playing ball games on deck. Others were relaxing or snoozing on steamer chairs or pursuing their individual interests.

After three days on board, Lucie was becoming accustomed to the ship's routine. Up around eight, for breakfast; stroll around the deck and watch the seagulls during the course of the morning. Have luncheon around one and dinner anytime from six in the evening.

Today, as on each of the days they had been aboard, the ship's bugler called passengers to their meals. Lucie estimated there were around five hundred people filing into the two compartments of the Third Class dining saloon.

Dennie said the ship was moving faster and faster every day: he could tell from its movement, and from the foaming waters below. It must be near top speed, he estimated. He was so clever, thought Lucie and she so stupid, by comparison.

Word went round that they had already travelled more than a thousand miles. Lucie could not conceive such a distance.

Her home was about five miles from the harbour and a few hundred from London. That was all she knew. The idea of putting such a great space between herself and Papa was really thrilling.

Something exciting had happened today. They saw the ship's captain and several of his uniformed officers striding along the corridors and decks. The captain was a most important looking bearded gentleman, resplendent in his uniform, with several medals jingling on his chest

Every day, he led his entourage of equally smartly dressed officers around the ship to inspect it, but this was the first time Lucie and Dennie had seen them so closely. The captain's name was Smith, whispered Dennie. Captain Edward Smith; known at E.J. He was a well respected captain: very proud of his ship

When he had moved out of earshot, someone said this was to be his last journey before retiring from the sea, for good. Lucie continued to watch the entourage stride, ever so purposefully, along the corridors and public rooms; nodding here, smiling there, saying good morning, and saluting those who greeted them.

A most impressive group of uniformed officers, they reminded Lucie of a photograph in Papa's study, in which a longdead ancestor had led a similar group of officers, only in his case, it was the Army. And they were going to war. She was not sure which one. Napoleonic, would it have been? In Santa Lucia

Where was Santa Lucia, anyway? It sounded like it might be in Italy, but then again, she thought Papa had said the sternlooking gentleman in the portrait had gone to the Americas. Oh never mind, it hardly mattered now. She was useless at geography. The subject, like most of those taught by her governess, had bored her to tears.

She would not have minded being taught geography, or anything else, by those handsome officers.

Lucie had never known either grand papa, because both had died before she was born. Mama's papa was never spoken of. She had seen pictures of Papa's papa: a tall, thin man in uniform, who had died rather suddenly. Perhaps he too was in the Army.

Papa had some brothers serving Kind and Country. One was in the Navy. She knew him by sight and, now that she came to think of it, he strongly resembled one of Captain Smith's officers parading round this ship. Thank goodness he hadn't seen her when they were doing their inspection. She must make sure he never did. Just in case it WAS her uncle. . .

"Hello, Lucie...." The Voice greeted her right out of the blue. "What are you doing now?"

"Just thinking," she told it.

"What are you thinking about?"

"Oh...." she was going to explain about grand papa and ask if The Voice knew where Saint Lucia was, but thought better of it. "Nothing." she lied.

"How is Stennie?"

She paused a moment and half smiled at the mention of the name. Why should she divulge her true circumstances to The Voice

"He is well, thank you."

"And yourself?"

"I am well, too."

"Are you still on board ship?"

Of course she was still on board ship. Where did The Voice think she was: out walking on the water?

"I am STILL on board ship," she stated.

"Are you enjoying the journey?"

"I am now!"

"Is that because you are no longer alone?"

"That is so." She stretched out luxuriantly on the chair, pulled the travel rug over her knees, smiled at Dennie, and placed her small white hand over her mouth while she tried, unsuccessfully, to suppress a yawn.

Travelling, she remarked, was tiresome. The Voice agreed, and she became aware of it telling her to drift off to sleep.

The next time it tried to make contact with her was at a most inconvenient moment. A most intimate moment.

"Oh go away," she told it.

Obediently, it left her alone until she and Dennie had made their plans for tomorrow and bade each other goodnight. Then she heard it again; actually apologising for interrupting her when she had obviously been busy.

"Busy?" she trilled. "Whatever do you mean?"

"You were otherwise engaged," it suggested.

"Yes, I was," she agreed.

Sunday morning was shivery cold.

Lucie donned her blue dress again. It was not a very warm garment, but she had worn her various changes of clothing and this WAS her Sunday best. She fondled the gold locket around her neck and uttered a silent prayer for Mama.

Divine Service was being held for those in the habit of worshipping on the Sabbath, but Lucie did not care to attend. Dennie was not interested in that one, because it was for worshippers of a different creed.

Instead, he dragged Lucie along to the service for his own Faith: a Mass, with much standing up, kneeling down and genuflecting. All the prayers and hymns were in Latin. . .

Their afternoon was most enjoyable. The rapidly dropping temperature gave them the perfect excuse for huddling together for warmth. But there was a limit to how long they could stay out of doors: it was becoming icy cold. Lucie's teeth began to chatter and she tucked in appreciatively to her warm, nourishing dinner.

Lucie listened to the strains of music pouring forth from the ship's orchestra and thought she recognised excerpts of Rossini, Verdi and a selection of operatic airs. Out on deck again, she hummed her happy accompaniment.

Alas, she could not stay outside for long.

The temperature was dropping dramatically. Even Dennie noticed, and suggested they retire for the night.

"What are you doing now, Lucie?" asked The Voice

"I am admiring the stars.... thousands of stars up there, twinkling down on us. But no moon. I can't see the moon. Just the stars." She glanced downwards, expecting to see pitch black water, but instead noticed the reflection of the stars in its glassy depths. The sight enchanted her. "I see them in the water, too. They are very pretty. Twinkling, like Christmas lights..." She stopped short.

The wailing woman was off again. This time, she came racing out on deck in her nightgown, surrounded by several of her friends.

She had had a dream in which she saw everyone on the ship being thrown into the water. Silly woman, thought Lucie, whose own dreams made no sense either.

But the difference between Lucie and this hysterical woman was that Lucie did not go around shouting out that everyone was doomed, and causing widespread panic among those who woke up in alarm.

Couldn't someone shut her up; tell her it was unbecoming to behave in that way? Order her back to her cabin?

Heavens above... what was that?

The starry, cloudless sky suddenly became hazy and the air was no longer clear. Lucie leaned over the railings, but all she could see now was pitch blackness, which brought back that twinge of apprehension. Even as she looked, she felt a strange vibration beneath her. She saw something large and white collide with the side of the ship. The object was almost immediately below her and was surrounded by an eerie light that seemed to be coming from deep inside it. Her apprehension gave way to real fear.

The impact reverberated right through the vessel, making it swerve which, in turn, knocked Lucie's head against one of the railings' pillars. She lost her balance and was temporarily disorientated.

Having regained her footing, she leaned over the railings once more and saw to her horror that the mysterious white object had moved to a different position and was beginning to give out the sickening sounds of fractured metal. She watched, horrified, as the object's icy fingers ran along the length of the ship. The stomach-churning sounds of scrunching and crunching gradually receded until, at last, the object calmly moved off.

Lucie noticed with a shiver, that it was still surrounded by its eerie light. What on earth was it? Had she witnessed a ghost? Well, if she had, so had several other passengers and there was much consternation as they tried solve the mystery.

The ship was reducing its speed.... slower, slower, until its great engines stopped altogether. More passengers and some members of the crew began to gather on the deck. The question everyone wanted answering was why a great ship like this should stop in the middle of the ocean, in the dead of night?

The hysterical woman had her answer ready. Hadn't she told everyone that the ship was doomed? She knew it for certain, the moment her rosary beads had fallen overboard. The ship would never reach New York, she insisted.

How long did Lucie stand transfixed, staring into the water? Five minutes, ten? Half an hour? An hour? More? Dazed, bemused, and missing her dear, sweet Dennie - whose sleeping quarters were still at the other end of the ship - she saw rockets being fired. She became vaguely aware of the deck beneath her tilting more and more.

She was in the middle of a nightmare.

"Dennie!" she cried out. "Dennie, darling, where ARE you. Help me, please..."

But it was not Dennie who answered.

"What is happening, Lucie?" asked The Voice, in a tone of real concern.

"I don't know," she cried. "I am cold... so very, very cold." Her teeth began chattering and goose pimples crept all over her body. "And I am frightened. Something is wrong...."

"What is it that's wrong, Lucie?"

"The ship.....there is water everywhere water.....WATER ALL OVER THE FLOOR, and I have lost one of my shoes....help me,.....please Help me find my shoe."

She watched groups of people running in every direction. Officers were telling them to put on life jackets and go to the boats. Lucie did not know where to find a life jacket and which way were the boats? Adults were screaming; children were crying and Lucie felt that if only she could find Dennie, everything would be all right.

The water came closer and closer until she was almost swimming in it.

"Help me.... help me..." she cried; but her voice was lost in the midst of all those other sounds of despair... sounds of people running, falling, crying, choking. If only she could find Dennie. The ship was now tilting at an alarming angle. Lucie, longing to be in the arms of her love, spilt tears into the icy waters of the North Atlantic. It suddenly occured to her that she might never see her darling sweetheart again.

She knew now with a sense of terrifying certainty that the huge, transatlantic liner was mortally wounded. Thanks to the ghostly white object she had witnessed rubbing itself so stealthily along the side of the ship, their dreams had been futile.

Would Lucie see her beloved Dennie before the ship sank to the bottom of the ocean?

She had almost given up hope when, to her amazement, she saw her love beckoning to her across the blackness. Delighted, she walked straight out to meet him. For one split second, their fingertips touched, then they were separated again.

Lucie took one long, terrified gulp and was no more.

On that bitterly cold April night, Lucie, Lady Latymer - otherwise known as Miss Mary Lennon - confronted Death and was unable to match its power. .

"Where are you, Lucie?"

She could hear The Voice, but she could not respond. Even if she could, she would have been unable to state where she was; because she was nowhere. She was back in the tunnel where everything was quiet, still, and vaguely - ever so vaguely - familiar.

In this place of nothingness, she was enveloped in soft, velvety darkness. For no apparent reason, she felt herself floating - as before - through a long, dark tunnel. Drifting, drifting. . .

Gradually, a tiny beam of brightness penetrated the black and it began to create shadows. The grey became misty and before she realised what was happening, the tunnel was flooded with light.

This was not the eerie light she had seen in the middle of the ocean, but a benevolent beam: bright and friendly. That other was evil, this was good.

She felt herself being propelled forward towards it .... being guided to keep moving forward... drifting, drifting....

"... until you find a happier set of memories," said the sound that was as familiar as the tunnel itself ...She was almost out of the watery tunnel. And now, suddenly, she was.

She was somewhere completely different: "Can you see where you are?" asked The Voice.

Glancing straight ahead, she attempted to focus, but all she could see was that everything was awash with light. Only it was not 'she' any more. Suddenly, inexplicably, it was me... MY Life Force, MY psyche, MY being. It was MY mind that was in motion now; hopping about, butterfly-style; registering, remembering, re-living.

I was there. Oh yes, I was there, all right: in a totally different lifetime to the one I had left a minute ago. A minute? A decade? A century? Time had totally collapsed in that tunnel. And time hardly mattered now, because there were so many other things to take in. Sounds were amplified. Sight was pin-sharp. I reached out, touched warmth and nestled comfortably against something furry. Happy sounds began coming from its tiny fluffy body. Then, from somewhere else: music filled the room; to re-awaken the rest of my senses. I could hardly contain my excitement as my eyes panned around. Streamers and balloons hung from the ceiling, people much larger than myself were bustling about, chatting, singing, and presenting me with prettily packaged parcels. The air was one of festivity. My eyes rested on the table, with its assorted cakes and sandwiches.

"Do you know where you are?"

"Yes," I heard myself respond in a squeaky little voice.

"Where are you?"

"I'm at home."

"What is your name?"

"My name is Monica, and I'm having a party. All my friends are coming".

Chapter 9

Where does all this leave us?

What conclusions - if any - can be drawn from the regression?

Before starting on the research proper, let's look at the clues provided by the young 'aristocrat' (if that was what she was).

Her name was Lucie Latymer. She kept insisting that her father was high born: a baron at least, possibly even an earl; though she did hint that not everyone accepted his status. Her mother appeared to have drowned in the garden pond. She had a governess whom she referred to as Miss Prim, but made no reference to any brothers and sisters; the implication being that she was probably an only child.

Although she had lived in various places as a small child, most of her life had been spent in a large white house, with a railway station at the end of the drive. The house was in a valley with a stream running through its orchard. The harbour was about five miles away and London a few hundred. She fell in love and ran away with a jobbing gardener, whom she referred to as Stennie. She subsequently transferred her affections to a man whom she thought of as Dennie, though she never actually uttered his name. No amount of coaxing would get her to identify either companion properly. Both men were cloaked in mystery.

It was not much to go on; making research into the regression mighty difficult. Lucie never mentioned the name of her home or its location.

Nor did she appear to know the name of the port from which she set sail or, if she did, she did not state it. The name of the ship never once passed her lips, nor did the fact that it was a maiden voyage; though her constant references to the liner's great size, her descriptions of life on board and her demise in the early hours of Monday, April 15, 1912, made it impossible to be any other than Titanic.

So... where does one start to look for a white house in the country with its own railway station, owned by a baron(?) named Latymer? With a 'y', as milady insisted.

The house, if it existed, was probably no longer standing, though one with a railway station at the end of the drive should provide some sort of clue.

It did not. During the period in question, railways were run by assorted private companies: all of which were subsequently nationalised, and many of which were closed down altogether, as we had anticipated, in the Beeching cuts of the sixties. Most of the small rural stations vanished without trace.

Lucie's station, like her house, had probably long gone.

As for her mysterious man friend, there would hardly be much point in trying to trace him. If he was a jobbing gardener, he probably had little or no roots (sic!).

So, not having the remotest idea of what part of the country the elusive Lucie hailed from, it seemed more sensible to make the name Latymer my starting point: see if there actually was such a barony and, if so, whether there had been any family disagreement over it. Frankly, I did not hold out much hope.

After that, I could go looking for any records of Lucie herself. Then, I intended to check with Titanic historians as to whether there had been any passengers aboard named Denis and Mary Lennon; probably travelling steerage.

It had already been established that no one name Latymer or Stenning was on the passenger lists: the chief steward's name was Latimer - with an i -, but that could be discounted. Anyway, he was male!

One of the few aristocratic passengers making that fateful journey did have a name similar to that of my alter-ego; well a first name, anyway. But Lady Lucile Duff-Gordon could be immediately discounted, too, because both she and her husband Sir Cosmo were among those who were saved.

Sticking with 'my' Lucie, therefore, I began my quest with a visit to the library to browse through Burke's Peerage. The aristocratic connection should be relatively easy to prove.... or disprove. . .

Meanwhile, Geoff Whitfield was doing his own investigations.

In the summer of 1990, he put out a plea through the Oracle Teletext Ltd. - a system then provided by the British independent television network, to search for missing people. Geoff had used this method on many occasions to build up his growing list of passengers on board, and their family backgrounds.

This time, he asked for anyone named Latimer (Latymer?) with Titanic connections to make contact with him.

He received some astonishing information.

Over to Geoff himself, to discover what happened next:

"On July 18, I had a telephone call from a Mrs Alice Lewis, who thought it likely that her sister, Eleanor Truelove Latimer (Geoff's spelling) was drowned while a passenger on the Titanic.

"Mrs Lewis was born in 1903 and her sister some years earlier. The family, who were farmers, resided in Cornwall.

"Eleanor Latimer was a headstrong girl, considered to be one of the most attractive in the area. For some time, unknown to her parents, Arthur Stenning, a farm labourer of gypsy descent, had been paying attention to her.

"During early April, 1912, Arthur, Eleanor and a young girl named Sarah Jane, who helped about the farm, set off to visit an aunt of the family in Saint Austell.

"During the journey, Eleanor informed them that she had to meet some friends in Probus, and would continue alone to her aunt's home. When she had not arrived by late evening, the family became alarmed and a message was dispatched to the Latimer's home early next morning.

"Mrs Lewis implied that the maid, Sarah Jane, was not as simple-minded as she pretended to be, and is convinced that the disappearance was contrived with her help.

"Meanwhile, Mr (?) Latimer pursued his errant daughter to Plymouth, where she had a number of friends, only to be told that Eleanor and Arthur had been there, but had departed for Southampton.

"Until now, Mr Latimer had not realised that his daughter was in the company of Arthur Stenning, whom he had employed several times, on a casual basis, to work on the farm. Fearing that the purpose of the visit to Southampton was elopment abroad, he visited the booking offices of the various shipping lines.

"A hastily dispatched telegram to Cornwall returned the news that Arthur Stenning had a brother in Scranton, Pennsylvania and it was thought that the couple may have been going there.

"At the White Star Line shipping office, the booking clerk remembered selling two steerage tickets aboard the Titanic, which was bound for New York, to a man who resembled Stenning's description. Of course, he had no way of knowing whether the pair were listed under assumed names or not, as only those who were emigrating had to prove their identity. He was unable to identify Eleanor from photographs, as Stenning - if indeed it was he - was alone when buying the tickets.

"Enquiries were made both at home and in America, but neither of the runaways nor Stenning's brother was heard from again.

"Mrs Lewis told me that she can, to this day, remember the awful uncertainty of not knowing for certain what had become of her only sister. Her parents' grief was soon overshadowed with shame as a rumour soonn sprang up that Eleanor had been 'in a delicate condition'.

"Mr Latimer ordered that all trace of his daughter be removed from the family home and Alice was never allowed to mention her name again."

Imagine the excitement that message caused... but it was tinged with frustration when I learned that the lady had finished her narrative and replaced the receiver without providing an address or telephone number where she could be contacted for further information.

Nevertheless, it was an important breakthrough; despite the fact that there were many discrepancies between Mrs Lewis' story and my own hypnotically recalled past-life memories.

First of all, the missing girl's name was Eleanor, not Lucie, and this was her sister, Alice, speaking. She also mentioned a lady's maid name Sarah Jane; but Lucie only ever referred to a governess, whom she called Miss Prim.

Also, she referred to parents (plural); suggesting that the mother was still alive at the time of the elopment. Friends in Probus never arose in any of the regressions.

Mrs Lewis' reference to Southampton was, of course, purely speculative. The booking clerk's recognition of someone resembling

Arthur's desciption is spurious, to say the least. How many tall, dark, handsome are there (were there) around?

Although Lucie did, apparently, have an intimate relationship with Arthur, she never, at any time, gave the impression that she was - as Mrs Lewis so quaintly put it - in a delicate condition.

Yet, uncannily, many of the other points raised DO concur with Lucie's story; the most exciting being reference to Arthur Stenning. Surely this was the 'Stennie', who had stolen Lucie's heart?

The girl's date of birth was not given. Under regression, Lucie felt about 17 at the time of the tragedy. However, being a headstrong and immature young lady, she may well have been older: possibly even in her early twenties. As yet, there was no way of telling.

She did run off with Arthur Stenning (goose pimples ran down my spine when his name was presented to me like that) He did work for Lucie's father and Lucy, at least, DID set sail on Titanic. Mrs Lewis, if she is still around, can take my word for that.

So where could we go from here?

Geoff, by now as confused as myself, decided to try the television search method once more. A further plea was put out on Teletext on 14 January, 1992, asking Mrs Lewis to provide more information about her long-lost sister; but it produced nothing. She never made contact again. If she is still alive, the lady would now be in her nineties.

If you're out there, Mrs Lewis, it would be wonderful to hear from you.

Having established Cornwall as the country seat of Mr (or Baron) Latymer, Geoff then wrote to several newspapers in the West Country to see if any further information could be gleaned... but again, without success. . .

Nevertheless, some of our investigations were producing results. To my utter astonishment - and great delight - my flick through Burke's Peerage proved relatively fruitful. The barony of Latymer (note... spelt with a y) DID exist.

The genuine, historical circumstances are as follows:

The Baronetcy was founded in 1431 and the Complete Peerage (Doubleday 1901 - 1938) provides the background to its three hundred year lapse (from the late 16th to the early 20th century).

'Latymer, Barony by Writ (Coutts Nevill)... This Barony, which fell into abeyance in 1577, was called out of abeyance by Francis Burdett Money Coutts (later Coutts-Nevill) by the issue to him of a writ of Summons to Parliament, 11 February, 1913.'

The entry goes on to explain that the gentleman in question was born on 18 September, 1852, married Edith Ellen Churchill on 15 April, 1875, and died on 8 June, 1923; to be succeeded by his only son and heir: Hugh Burdett Money-Coutts. Hugh was born on 13 August, 1876 and married Hester Francess Russell on 11 June, 1900.

Flicking back briefly to the sixteenth century, we find that the fourth baron and his baroness had four daughters (Katharine, Dorothy, LUCY and Elizabeth). But there was no male issue from that marriage, which was why the barony went into abeyance. Let us look at Lucy. Born in 1549, she married Sir William Cornwallis of Brome in Suffolk and they, too, had four daughters: Frances, Elizabeth, Cornelia and Anne. Lucy died on 30 April, 1609; leaving her daughters as co-heirs, and was not heard of again until 1911, when she was represented for the Barony of Latymer, by Francis Burdett Thomas Money Coutts, as already explained.

By curious co-incidence, the man who brought the barony out of abeyance also had four daughters; though, fortunately for the family line, he did also have a son and heir: the above-mentioned Hugh.

Perhaps Francis had two more children: Lucy and Alice?

If he had, their births do not appear to be documented; though oddly enough, the name Lucy does tend to pop up from time to time in the Latymer family.

Turning the pages of history back once more to the sixteenth century, we find that the lady who married John (Nevill) Fourth Lord Latymer, was also named Lucy. She was the second daughter of Henry (Somerset) Earl of Worcester, and the marriage took place in 1545.

At some point, she changed the spelling of both her Christian name and her surname. Mr Money-Coutts told me his source - Burke's Peerage - appeared to differ slightly from Doubleday. When she died, widowed on the 23rd February 1581 or 1582 she asked for an alabaster tomb to be decorated with pictures of herself and her four daughters.

What style. . .

Let us come forward once more - this time, three hundred and forty years - for the publication of another Will... that of the Fifth Baron

Latymer (Francis Burdett Money Coutts, mentioned earlier). Though, before doing so, it might be worth mentioning that THIS Francis was a minor Victorian poet and not to be confused with his grandfather Sir Francis Burdett (1770 - 1844), the Radical Member of Parliament.

Here is an extract from The Times, dated 25 July, 1923:

'The Rt. Hon. Francis Burdett Thomas, Fifth Baron Latymer, of 15 Hanover Square West and late of 440 Strand, WC, a partner in Coutts and Co., bankers and author of numerous poems and other works - one of the founders of the Girls' Friendly Society died, aged 70.'

The report goes on to state that he left in excess of a million pounds gross and that one of the beneficiaries was a Nurse Mary Granger 'to whom I am under a debt of gratitude'.

Nurse Granger was given the use of his town flat and effects for life and a life annuity of £1,000. He left £40,000 to each of his four daughters and the remainder of his estate to his son and heir.

In view of the fact that the address of the Fifth Baron Latymer was mentioned in Doubleday as 'Stoodleigh, in the county of Devon', I thought it might be worth my while writing to the vicar of the parish church to determine whether the births or christening of two sisters had been recorded in parish registers.

The Reverend Roderick Thorp responded thus:

"There are no references in our Baptismal Register to either Eleanor Truelove or Alice. On 16 May, 1910, Hugh Burdett and Hester Frances Money-Coutts had a daughter, Mercy Burdett, baptised. Mr Money-Coutts is described as a banker.

"I can find no other mention of the family in the church records."

He added that their home - Stoodleigh Court - had been a preparatory school since 1926.

The next letter I wrote was to the school itself, and even as I penned the enquiry, that strong impression of a large white manor house kept revolving in my brain. Could THIS be Lucie's ancestral home, I wondered... albeit that it was in Devon, and Mrs Lewis' had mentioned the adjoining county of Cornwall.

A few days later, a charming and most helpful letter arrived from Ravenswood School, Stoodleigh Court. Attached to the letter was a prospectus. The picture on the cover featured a large, impressive building which (however hard I tried to hammer the pieces of the jigsaw to make them fit) was definitely NOT the white house I had envisaged.

Much as I would have liked to implant Lucie there, I was absolutely certain she had never lived in this former baronial hall. Stoodleigh Court was not the building for which I searched: it was far too grand.

I would have to widen the net.

Would any of Baron Latymer's descendants be able to help? Mr David Money Coutts, for example? I wrote to him, thus:

"If my records are correct, you are the great-grandson of Francis Burdett Thomas Money Coutts, late of Stoodleigh, in Devon, who called the Barony of Latymer out of abeyance on 11 February, 1913.

"I am looking for any information which might be available on two Latymer sisters living around that time: i.e., Eleanor Truelove (who may have been known as Lucie), born in 1895 and Alice, a few years younger.

"I understand that Alice is still living and her married name is Lewis; but do not know where she is. I have read through several back copies of The Times, but can find no reference to these sisters. Did your great-grandfather happen to have a brother? Could the sisters be cousins of your late grandfather?"

In case Mr Money-Coutts wondered what was behind my strange line of questioning, I told him about my regression to Lucie and her demise.

He replied in a matter of days.

"Thank you for your letter about my great grandfather, Francis Money-Coutts, Lord Latymer," he wrote. "He was not 'of Stoodleigh': that was his son Hugh, my grandfather.

"Francis had four half-brothers and three half-sisters, none of them Eleanor or Alice and, of course, their surname was plain Money.

"Only Francis and his mother changed their name to MoneyCoutts. Latymer is the title that he reclaimed, but was never a family name: that was originally Nevill.

"Francis had four daughters: no Alice, but one was Eleanor Burdett..."

Mr Money-Coutts added whimsically that 'his' Eleanor had married a gentleman named Eric Walter Carr and had lived respectably this side of the Atlantic until her death in 1966.

So much for 'my' Eleanor, or Lucie, her gypsy lover and their dramatic demise in April, 1912.

"Sorry," continued Mr Money Coutts, but I don't know who your Eleanor (Lucie) and Alice are; though his curiosity was obviously aroused, for he asked: "Do you have any written evidence of their existence?"

It grieved me to do so, but I had to admit that unfortunately no, I had not!

Mr Money-Coutts further made the point that if Eleanor were born in 1895, it hardly seemed likely that her family would have used the name Latymer 13 years before the 1912 resolution of the House of Lords recognising Francis as a co heir to the title.

Far be it from ME to suggest that the sisters could be my correspondent's great-aunts on the wrong side of the blanket. Even if they were, Mr Money-Coutts would hardly know anything about them almost a century after their respective - if not exactly respectable - conceptions.

Could he assist in my search for the white house?

"I can confirm that Stoodleigh is a very dark house, but it didn't belong to Francis anyway."

A thought: "His father-in-law's house in Weybridge may have been white and manorial, but his father's house certainly was not."

My gut feeling was that Weybridge, being in a totally different part of the country, was way off course for Lucie.

"Sorry I can't help more," concluded my most helpful correspondent, "but as far as I know, the only Lucy (his spelling) to be the daughter of a Lord Latymer so far has been Lucy Cornwallis, daughter of the Fourth Baron."

NOTE, CHAPTER NINE

*1 The reason why there appears to be come confusion over the year that the 16th century Lucie, Lady Latymer, died is that this was before the changeover in 1752 from the Julian to the Gregorian calendar. Mr Money Coutts offers an explanation: "The Julian year began on 25 March, so the February date was 1582 under the Gregorian calendar, 1581 under the Julian." Burke's Peerage gives the date of the lady's death as 1581/2: Doubleday, as 1582/3.

Chapter 10

Southampton was the obvious place for me to visit next. It was where Titanic set off from and Mrs Lewis had seemed to think that was where her sister and Arthur had boarded the ship.

In a desperate attempt to jog my memory further, I visited the city. Geoff, who was by now as hooked on the story as I was myself, very kindly drove me there and introduced me to his friend and fellow THS member, Brian Ticehurst.

Brian, who is an expert on the history of his city, and the author of a book about its Titanic memorials[*1], devoted an entire day to escorting me around: first stop, the dockside.

We stood on the very spot where the boat train (the Titanic special) carrying passengers from London's Waterloo station would have arrived.

I looked around, but the territory was totally unfamiliar. Was he SURE this was the spot, I asked, idiotically?

Nothing would shake my conviction that, on stepping off the train, Lucie had travelled uphill towards a promenade. Where was the row of hotels, and what had happened to the sweeping lawns?

Brian reminded me of the extensive damage Southampton had suffered during the Second World War, As a result, many of the old properties had disappeared long ago. There might well have been an hotel somewhere with a canopy stretching out over the pavement, he added; though he did not know of one answering that description. Would I like him to investigate?

No, thank you, I told him. This line of enquiry already seemed like a lost cause. I apologised for wasting his time.

I looked long and hard at the spot where Titanic had been moored, and Brian showed me exactly where passengers would have stepped straight from the dockside on to the ship. My heart sank even further. Nothing looked, or felt, even remotely familiar.

What about the little boats going out to sea, I ventured?

We strolled along to where the tugs moved the great liner outwards. Still no joy. I gazed blankly at the point on the grey water where she turned, headed downstream, and off out into St George's Channel; at the other side of which she picked up some more passengers at Cherbourg.

By now, the only certainty in my mind was that Lucie had never been HERE.

Ever hopeful, Brian took me on a conducted tour of the city, but nothing at all clicked. He was doing his best to sort out my muddled memories, but sadly, they were totally dormant. After a fabulous meal with his wife Janet and himself, Geoff delivered me back to Merseyside, more confused than ever.

Knowing now that Lucie would not have boarded at Cherbourg, there was only one other place left: Queenstown (since renamed Cobh).

I had no conscious knowledge of the place, never having been there in this life; but, fortunately, I knew someone who lived in Youghal, which my map of Ireland showed to be in the same county and not terribly far away.

Tom Williams is a shipping correspondent and another Titanic buff. He first made contact with me after reading one of my books[*2] and suggested that if I were planning any more, he would be delighted to help with the research.

Taking him at his word, I sent him a questionnaire, which he attended to immediately. I reproduce it verbatim..

MOH: How much of the old harbour at Cobh remains as it was in 1912?

TW: Most of it. It is slightly more dilapidated, with grass growing through the concrete, but is easily recognisable.

MOH: Would you know whether, in 1912, there would have been much in the way of sea traffic between our two countries? Could someone have crossed, even aboard a cattle ship, from anywhere along the south west coast of England, or Wales, to anywhere in or around Cork... even to Cobh itself?

TW: Considerable sea traffic passed between Ireland and England - particularly the west coast of England; because of Welsh coal mining and other industrial pursuits. At that time, Ireland was part of the Commonwealth and there was a massive British Army presence here. As a result, there would be continuous traffic to and fro: particularly to Queenstown, where there was a large garrison.

MOH: Were there - are there still - many bed and breakfast places in or around Cobh where Titanic passengers might have spent the night? I am thinking mainly of steerage.

TW: Yes. Steerage passengers would have stayed a night or two at any of the bed and breakfast places which still operate in Cobh. Titanic dropped her port anchor at the mouth of Queenstown harbour, about two miles out, at exactly 11.30 a.m. on Thursday, April 11.

One hundred and thirteen third class and seven second class passengers boarded from the tenders. They also put on board 1,385 bags of mail. Seven passengers disembarked. Titanic left on her crossing at exactly 1.30 p.m. with approximately 2,227 passengers and 885 crew on board, though the exact number of passengers has never been accurately defined.

MOH: Would it be possible for me to stay in the sort of bed and breakfast establishment where an eloping couple might have stayed in 1912; or is that now the 'red light' district of the town, as I understand it to be in Southampton?

TW: There is no red light district in Cobh! Nor has the town any crime rate. The people are lovely. The town has many guest houses and hotels. Your most likely contact would be the Commodore Hotel, as this was where several passengers bought their Titanic tickets, and actually stayed for a few days. The Commodore overlooks Cork harbour and was originally known as the Queens. According to a local history of the town,[*3] it was built on the site of a woden pavilion to receive Queen Victoria as she landed from her royal yacht. The town was originally called Cove, but after the Royal visit, was changed to Queenstown. In 1920, the local council changed it back, only now to the Gaelic form of the name: spelt Cobh, but still pronounced Cove.

MOH: Do we know if there WERE any eloping couples actually setting off from Queenstown: and if so, are any details available?

TW: Yes, there were believed to be several. Details not available.

MOH: Would passengers have bought their tickets on the day of sailing, or would they have had to book them in advance?

TW: Most booked in advance, but there were still plenty on the day.

MOH: Were there many people waving off the passengers as they boarded the tenders...sitting on benches, strolling along the promenade..., and so on?

TW: Yes, thousands. It was the day of the Cork Summer Show, so the area was crammed with people.

MOH: As I understand it, the Angelus only rings out at 12 noon and 6p.m. In Queenstown, on the day Titanic dropped anchor, were the church authorities ringing it early with the specific purpose of upsetting the poor emigrants, was the church clock half an hour fast, or did one of their priests have some sort of inkling that he was ringing a death knell?

TW: The Angelus does normally ring out at noon and 6 p.m. But, apparently, on this day, ringing it at 11.30 represented a sort of 'goodbye' to the emigrants and 'hello' to the world's largest ship.

MOH: Did one of the emigrants play his pipes on the tender sailing outwards?

TW: Yes, his name was Eugene Daly. He played them on the pier (he had just come out of a local watering hole and was probably feeling mellow). He attempted to play them on the tender, but with the pitching and tossing and his own uncertain state, the sounds must have been decidedly odd. He also played on board Titanic.

The positive answers to all these questions were the best break I had had yet. I was, naturally, wild with excitement. There was only one course of action open to me now.

That visit to Cobh suddenly became top priority. I couldn't wait to see what I might find there.

NOTES, CHAPTER 10

*1 Ticehurst, Brian: The Titanic, Southampton's Memorials, Kingfisher Railway Productions (1990)

*2 O'Hara, Monica: Hands Off The Titanic, Countyvise (1989)

*3 Broderick, Mary, A History of Cobh, Broderick (1989), pp 110-111.

PART TWO

Chapters 11 - 13

COBH

(formerly Queenstown)

Chapter 11

During the flight to Dublin, I found my thoughts drifting of their own accord to the hotel with the canopy. Even as my mind dwelt upon it, the image became clearer. It was in a place called West.. something and next door to an establishment, the nature of which my mind appeared to be blocking. I could not fathom why.

So I continued to let spontaneous memories of 'my' hotel enter my head. The image of the canopy became clearer and clearer in my mind. I could see how beautifully decorated it was, and how it extended from the front door of the hotel (the name of which still eluded me) right out to the edge of the pavement, where it was supported by two pillars.

I could feel myself standing at the entrance with my escort and being attended to by liveried doormen. How much of this was real memory, and how much imagination, I asked myself?

Could Lucie Latymer be another Bridey Murphy? Forty years earlier, Bridey had made her appearance in circumstances not unlike those in which Lucie was now 'manifesting' herself.

In 1956, Morey Bernstein, an amateur hypnotist living in America, published a book[*1] in which he described how he had regressed a Colorado housewife named Virginia Tighe to nineteenth century Ireland. Mr. Bernstein claimed that, under hypnosis, Mrs Tighe (whom he referred to as Ruth Simmons) spoke in a lilting Irish brogue of a place she had seemingly never visited in this life. Throughout various regressions, she gave the names of several Irish people and places.

Naturally, the Press of its day went wild with excitement. But the regression was ultimately shown to be just a shade off course. For it transpired that Mrs Tighe's unconscious was making her re-enact stories narrated to her, as a child, by an aunt who came from Cork. Then that too was disputed. This very complicated case is fully explained by Roy Stemman in Reincarnation International.*[2]

The lady was not consciously cheating: merely giving vent to her over-active imagination. And, at this point, it has to be said that I too spent part of my childhood in Ireland: though much further north, in a county called Cavan. In any case, my elder sister Doirin stated quite emphatically that we had never visited Cobh as children. Summer holidays were invariably spent in a place called Skerries, near Dublin.

The plane began its descent, but I was still on a high. I felt very strongly that I was going to find my hotel within the next twenty-four hours: or if not actually the place itself, at least hard evidence to show that it was as I 'saw' it.

We touched down just in time for me to race across the airport to catch my Cork-bound 'plane and during that second flight, I really was in the clouds, in every sense. The 'vibes' became stronger and stronger. In Cork, I shot across the city to catch the earliest available train to Cobh, only to find there was not one for almost three hours.

Titanic passengers would have kicked up a right old shindig if they had to wait so long. However, the delay did provide me with an opportunity to soak up the atmosphere of the railway station, which looked as if it had hardly changed in a hundred years.

Better still, I could now sense Lucie's presence strongly. She had been here... I just KNEW it!

Sight of me taking several photographs fascinated an elderly gentleman, who volunteered the information that the front of the station used to be the back and vice versa. Ah yes, this was Ireland, all right.

"Where the car park is now, the horses and carriages used to line up," he told me. "Foot passengers would come through that side gate (now sealed off) and down the ramp (now blanketed with snow), where they would join those coming off the hackneys.

"Then off they'd all go through yon white wooden gate that leads straight on to the platform. (The white gate was also now out of use). The track runs right along the coast to Cobh. 'Tis a lovely, scenic route," he concluded fondly.

Well it was one I was not destined to see today. Thanks to the continued bad weather, the train was not running and a bus had been put on instead. Its windows were frozen on the outside, steamed up on the inside and I could see very little of anything.

Half an hour later, we pulled up at Cobh harbour; alongside the Deepwater Quay. Those I asked said this was the very spot from where the tenders sailed out to Titanic.

Surely they were mistaken?

This scene was nothing like the place I remember... if Lucie sailed from Queenstown, which I strongly suspected she did, where was the wooden jetty? Where was the promenade with its trees, benches, bandstand and gun carriages?

Bandstand and gun carriages? What on earth suddenly brought them into my mind?

Lucie's memories were coming through loud and clear.. find the terraced row of hotels, the promenade, the jetty, and I would find my gadfly.

Could the driver point me in the direction of the promenade? (Note the confident use of the definite article. Not 'a', but 'THE' promenade)

"Up the hill," he pointed.

As I began walking, the place became increasingly familiar. Half way up that steep and exceedingly icy hill, I froze... and it was not because of the weather. As the Low Road (this one) met up with the High Road, the emotional charges within me produced a series of wildly exciting shocks.

When I climbed up into Westbourne Place I was hit, full frontal, with a blast from the past. This was the very hill up which the two horses had panted their way from the railway station as they transported our two lovers in the hansom cab. This was the very route along which Lucie and her love travelled almost eight decades ago.

Following in their footsteps was one of the most emotionally-charged experiences of my life. Oh yes, Lucie, you were here all right. This was where you came after running away from home. And what did I see at the top of the hill?

Right first time.

The promenade with benches, the row of guest houses and hotels, gardens, the bandstand, and the gun carriage. To my ecstatic delight, they were all there. Well, almost all... as yet, I could not see my dream hotel, with the canopy. I would find it, though. I was not going to leave this place, until I did.

Tingling excitement crept over me as my dream became concrete reality. I knew this place like the back of my hand, and would need no maps to guide me: even the wooden hot dog stand looked strangely familiar.*3

Oh come on, Monica, I told myself, now you ARE letting your imagination run away with you. They did not have hot dogs in those days. Be sensible.

But being sensible was not easy under such circumstances. I felt like a child waking up on Christmas morning with a sackful of toys. Sight of this lovely, lovely town was my gift from the gods. I had a sudden urge to shout 'eureeka'.

Here I was in Cobh, then: and what a splendid place it was. Situated on the southern shore of Cork, the former health resort and watering place had a look of Brighton, the popular resort on the south coast of England.

I wanted to believe I stayed here at a time when it was known as Queenstown. All my instincts told me that some part of my being was aboard Titanic. But, by nature, I am a sceptic. Being a journalist, I have to be.

The crucial issue at stake was: could I prove beyond a shadow of doubt that some inherent part of me - of my memories - was alive in the early part of the century and that whoever it was plunged, with the great liner, to the depths of the North Atlantic in April 1912?

The Commodore Hotel was to be my home for the next three days and, grand though it was, it had no domed, canopied entrance. Nor did it look as if it ever had one, although the hotel itself was certainly here at the time of Titanic, as I already knew.

To guests setting off for, or returning from, a trans-Atlantic trip, the name of this hotel would have been highly appropriate; for, in the early days of this century, it was known the States.

My suite of rooms overlooking the harbour provided a magnificent view, but no memories of Lucie and Stennie. Having dispensed with my luggage and freshened up, I went off out again, armed with camera, pen and notepad.

For the next hour or so, I occupied myself taking pictures and writing down impressions of everything in sight. The more I saw of the seafront, the promenade, the row of houses, the more convinced I was that this was the place of my dreams: the place for which I had searched so long.

The bandstand had lost its elaborate roof, but the gun carriages had not changed. What on earth had they done to the pedestrian area, though? It was not at all as it used to be, having been modernised almost beyond recognition. Almost, but not quite...

A plaque in the corner provided the answer. Promenade Quay, it explained, was renamed Kennedy Park in 1963, following the visit to Ireland that year of the late John Fitzgerald Kennedy.

So that was why it felt 'out of synch'.

The palm trees - elegant though they were - formed no part of my mental image either: they, too, were comparatively new. Nevertheless, my memory of this part of town closely resembled the present day scene. There certainly were trees here at the time of Lucie's visit, but they were not palms.

The benches were wrong, too. Those I envisaged were of wrought iron: these were wooden; but then, these were probably installed when Kennedy Park was constructed. More and more evidence was accumulating.

Oh God, what had we here?

A rotting wooden pier; the water clearly visible beneath the slats... THIS was the memory which had been lodged in my unconscious for so long. THIS WAS THE VERY SPOT WHERE LUCIE'S TENDER SAILED FROM.

I was transfixed by the sight.

The memories began flooding into my mind as dramatically as the waters of the north-Atlantic flooded into that glorious ship. As I stood on those slats, I re-lived Lucie's fear that she would catch her heel and fall through to the water below (a premonition of what was to happen to her a few days later?)

I did not need to close in on that wooden jetty either with my camera or my trembling body. I DARED not close in on it: one look in that direction would bring back all the terror: albeit that the feeling itself could be removed by self-hypnosis, as taught by my husband back home.

Here, surely, was where Titanic's eloping couple set out from.

"No," insisted the local people I asked. "This is where Cunarders sailed from: White Star passengers set off from the Deepwater Quay down by the railway station."

Far be it from me to correct those who should know the history of their own town, but my gut feting told me they were wrong. Damn it all, I was THERE!

It was to be another three years before I was proved correct.*[4]

Next morning, I was awakened to the sound of bells. Saint Colman's cathedral was chiming out every quarter. If its 47-bell carrilon (the country's largest) made such sweet sounds when Lucie was here, she must have been equally enchanted. Then why did they ring no familiar bells for me, so to speak?*[5]

Breakfast over, I decided to wander around town in search of 'my' hotel. Most of the other disjointed memories had been retrieved and were beginning to slot into place, but this one remained elusive.

Back at the Commodore, Finbarr Lynch, the assistant manager, told me that 25,000 people visited the town last year for the visit of the QE2. Because, on that occasion, the liner's visit was to commemmorate the 150th anniversary of the founding of Cunard, she came right in to the quay.

Normally, she anchored at the harbour mouth, off Roches' Point (where Titanic had also dropped anchor). Lengthy and very expensive dredging had to be carried out to allow Cunard's flagship to come right into the pier. Her proximity to the harbour was, added Mr Lynch, a one-off and not expected to happen again.

Unfortunately, I was unable to take a boat trip around the bay because they did not run during the winter months. Even then, I would not be taken out to Roches' Point, because only the tenders ventured so far.

A few doors away from the Commodore, at Westbourne House, Sheila Denvir (honorary secretary of Cobh Tourism) told me about The Queenstown Project.

The purpose of the project was to create an historic theme town based on Cobh's maritime, emigration and railway history. Plans were already afoot to restore the old railway buildings and the Yacht Club. Apparently, in the days following the Potato Famine (1845 - '47), this county experienced a greater intensity of emigration than any other. Most of the young people setting off for England and America came through this station to catch their ships.

Mrs Denvir put me in touch with Joe Wilson, the town's photographer; his collection of old prints might prove interesting, she thought. An appointment was made for me to interview Captain Charles Nash, a lucid octogenarian seafarer who lived on the other side of town.

I was given to understand that the captain had a long memory and was always happy to share his extensive knowledge with researchers like myself. I was to see him next day.

Just as I was about to leave, Mrs Denvir gave me an old postcard view of the seafront, from which I noted that sure enough, the horse-drawn cabs DID make regular journeys to and from the railway station.

It was, apparently, common practice for hotels and guest houses to send porters to tout for business among incoming visitors. Some supplied cabs, others jaunting cars, while the less opulent establishments simply sent porters on foot, to carry passengers' luggage while they walked, as I had, up the hill. From a local newsagent, I purchased a book entitled A History of Cobh,*[6] and flicked through it briefly, with the intention of settling down to read it later on.

What I saw on page 151 resulted in a sudden intake of breath and an urgent need to sit down.

It was a picture of West Beach, with a row of hotels; but the one called The Imperial was what rooted me to the spot. IT HAD A CANOPIED ENTRANCE EXTENDING TO THE EDGE OF THE PAVEMENT, AND WAS AN EXACT REPRODUCTION OF THE ONE I HAD SEEN IN MY MIND'S EYE FOR SO LONG.

NOTES, CHAPTER 11

*1 Bernstein, Morey: The Search for Bridey Murphy, Doubleday, Toronto; Hutchinson, London (1956)

*2 Stemman, Roy: Reincarnation International, Jan, 1994, No.l, pp 18-21

*3 The hot dog stand WAS there at the time of Titanic's sailing; for the purchase of tea, coffee and soft drinks.

*4 White Star Journal (publication of the Irish Titanic Historical Society), Vol.2 No.2 (Summer 1994), p.3., reports: Third class passengers travelling from Queenstown on the Titanic reported to the office of James Scott and Co. on the morning of April 11, 1912. The tender America of the Clyde Shipping (carrying 113 passengers) was then boarded at the adjacent White Star Pier.

*5 St Colman's cathedral's carillon and clock were not installed until 1916. The Angelus bell pealing out over the bay would have been from one of the town's many churches.

*6 Broderick, Mary: A History of Cobh, Broderick (1989).

Chapter 12

My first task after breakfast on Sunday was to stroll along in the direction of the former Imperial Hotel (now the Atlantic Inn) at Number Eight, West Beach. A notice outside said they served lunches. Naturally, I intended to be there the minute the doors opened. And yet...

I wasn't sure that I should. I was half afraid of the memories such a visit might jar. Overcome with a mixture of unreasonable fear and wild, crazy excitement, I was at one and the same time thrilled and terrified at the prospect of stepping inside 'my' hotel. A bit like John Milton with his great epic poems, Paradise Lost and Paradise Regained.

How unfortunate that it was situated so close to something so terribly, er... in the words of Nancy Mitford, 'non-U.'"[1] Number Seven was the place my mind was blocking out. Why?

All was suddenly revealed when I discovered that the house next door to 'my' hotel, though now a rather pleasant-looking restaurant known as The Galley, used to be something very different.

Grace O'Brien was probably providing an invaluable service by opening up an Emigrants' Home; but it was hardly Lucie's style now, was it?

In its day, this house had also been a Post Office, and a rest home for soldiers and sailors. No wonder Lucie turned up her pert little nose.

While waiting for the doors of the Atlantic Inn to open, I wandered on towards the east end of town and upwards for a view of the beach once frequented by sailing ships, and popular with smugglers.

A century ago, this was the commercial centre of Cobh. It was from here the outbound emigrants embarked for the ships waiting at the harbour mouth. In the latter half of the nineteenth century, more than half a million people left Ireland; most of them through this port.

Cathedral bells continued to ring out the quarter. They made a lovely sound, though I now knew why it was not in the least nostalgic, the Angelus calling the faithful to prayer on that far off April day did not come from the cathedral.

Back in the main part of town, I examined the Lusitania Monument. An evocative structure featuring bronze figures of grief-stricken fishermen, surmounted by an Angel of Peace, the memorial was commissioned by Americans in memory of those who died when the liner was sunk by a German U-boat on 7 May, 1915, off the Old Head of Kinsale, a few miles down the coast. The tragedy resulted in the loss of fifteen hundred lives: a similar number to those lost on Titanic.

Cobh residents appeared to be much more emotionally involved with Lusitania than Titanic. Perhaps it was because the bodies of 139 Lusitania victims were brought here to be buried in the Old Churchyard on the hill: whereas Titanic victims and survivors were all taken to America.

I wandered back to the jetty, and was offered a trip home to Liverpool on what I mistakenly understood to be a yacht, but which turned out to be a five-man (and no woman!) cargo vessel.

I was tempted to accept passage on the thirty hour journey, but when I mentioned my Titanic obsession to the Captain, he withdrew the offer. Just as one should never mention the possibility of crashing to an airline pilot, it is bad luck to talk to ships' captains about a sinking. ANY sinking.

Back at the Atlantic Inn at noon, I plucked up my courage and stepped inside; to meet Leslie and Avril Casey, the proprietors. I explained that I was writing a book about a young woman who stayed in these premises for a night or two before sailing away on that memorable maiden voyage.

Would they, by any chance, happen to have the visitors' books dating back to 1912? No? Well, never mind. Perhaps it would be possible for me to see over the place, or at least, to be shown into a room where the young lady might have stayed?

Mrs Casey very kindly led me to the back of the inn, which was the oldest part of the building, and I was given a quick peek into one of the rooms no longer in use. I was assured that this wing had changed vey little over the years. To my great disappointment, I felt nothing. Nothing at all.

I was led to the first floor, through an old door, with the words 'coffee room' enscrolled on the frosted glass. This was now the dining room. The similarly-styled door of the adjoining lounge announced our entry into what used to be the drawing room. Despite the grand tour, I did not have the remotest feeling of familiarity. Had my memory cells gone to sleep? Or were they playing bewitching games with me? Why, why, WHY were they not operating as they should be? I was so tantalisingly close to finding what I wanted, yet it still eluded me. Oh Lucie, what tricks were you playing now?

Lunch was sumptuous but, though it grieved me to have to admit it 'my' hotel did not seem to be mine, after all. While the Atlantic Inn was a most pleasant family-run guest house and the service was excellent, it was not what I was looking for. What was wrong? Why could I not tune in to Lucie's feelings in here? Was I trying too hard?

Sated in body, if not in mind, I sauntered in the general direction of Holy Ground for my appointment with Captain Nash, the former harbour pilot. With a little time to spare, I strolled along in the general direction of the cinema, still trying to put my thoughts in order.

Suddenly, without warning, my skin began to tingle and the evocative whiff of carbolic hit whatever memory buds were lurking in my nostrils. Ha-ha, Lucie. Very funny.

You were supposed to be sharing the Imperial Hotel/ Atlantic Inn with me, not making me feel itchy and in need of a bath. I could do without this, thank you very much.

(It was not until much later in the day that I learned the reason for the carbolic smell assailing my nostrils. The cinema used to be a public baths' house and later an emigrant examination - or 'de-lousing' - station. As Lucie might have put it, how very unbecoming.)

A passage on the left led to Harbour Row where, still soaking up the soapy atmosphere, and still bemoaning the lack of nostalgia inside the hotel, I carried on, to climb up more steep hills, all like sheets of glass. The town of Cobh is a warren of steep inclines and narrow streets: a bit like Edinburgh.

On the plus side, the views were breathtaking. The place was so much prettier than I had ever imagined. No wonder local people became so upset when all those publications about Titanic only made passing reference to her final port of call.

"Not many authors ever bother to come to our town and talk to us," several of them claimed.*[2]

Built for naval officers and their wives, it was a very English type of town; yet its Irish element was as strong as anywhere else.

Captain Nash's home was high on a hill overlooking Roches' Point. He regaled me with wonderful tales of his days at sea. At eighty six years of age, he could remember the day Titanic sailed, as if it were only yesterday.

"I was eight at the time, and the town was full of people," he recalled. "I stood by this very wall where we're standing now. I was with my school-friends, neighbours and visitors. People poured into town from all over the country for a sight of the great ship. We had a grand view of her."

Had it been a very emotional experience, I asked, and was somewhat deflated to hear that no: as boys, they had regularly watched the big ships come and go.

Who, among those children, could have had any inkling of what was to come? As far as they were concerned, this was just another ship passing through: albeit, larger than most.

With hindsight, I could appreciate that this was a very natural reaction for a schoolboy. As far as Captain Nash knew, there had been no Cobh residents among the passengers or crew. All had converged here from other places.

The captain came from a long line of seafarers. His grandfather James, had been employed as a Cunard Line pilot for twenty years. His father, Thomas,had also been a harbour pilot, as were three of his uncles.

His son, Thomas, had recently retired after serving for several years as captain of tankers in South Africa, and his grandson, Charles, was a cadet at nautical school, Captain Nash was as knowledgeable about the sea as anyone I could have met.

Of my reluctance to walk along slippery wooden walkways, it occured to me to ask how secure the tenders' gangways might have been.

"They'd be wobbly," he assured me. "Particularly if there was a bit of a swell on the water."

"And was there a swell that day?"

"There was!"

Somehow, I thought there might have been.

Over a cup of tea, the captain showed me some fragile and yellowing documents, which revealed that, back in 1912, trans-Atlantic travellers could travel in from Cork with a pair of horses (landau, Brougham, Victoria, seating four inside), for five shillings. One horse Brougham or Victoria cost three shillings and sixpence per hour (17½p in decimal currency).

For visitors who wished to travel in by train, the first class single fare was one shilling and fourpence (approximately 8p); second class, one shilling; third class, eight pence (less than 4p).

The climate was described as being mild and equitable and the town itself 'a delighful spring residence for persons with delicate chests and for those convalescing from acute disease.'

The un-named writer continued: 'With fuschias, yuccas, geraniums and myrtles blossoming, invalids can exercise themselves throughout the year. Dr A Thompson - a well-known local specialist - is readily available. (What exactly for was not revealed). . .

Speaking of doctors, I had a very strange encounter when I visited the spot where the Lusitania victims were buried. A group of children thought I might be interested in the grave of Dr James Verling. The man, a native of Cobh, was surgeon to Napoleon during his exile on St Helena.

What the children wanted to show me was that, where the soil had partially subsided, his skull was clearly visible. If local children knew about this, the church authorities must also surely have known. Why could they not have re interred the remains? It was most disconcerting to be stared at in this way by a human skull... though some might say that it was no worse than to have Lucie beaming out her thoughts, also from what one might assume to be the Great Beyond.

At least, the Cobh children's behaviour was more subdued than that of their Liverpool counterparts when, in the 1930's, in the graveyard of the long-demolished Christ Church, an energetic group of youngsters was discovered playing cricket with some human remains.

They were those of William Windham Sadler, who had died almost a century earlier. Sadler, in 1817, had become the first man to cross the Irish Sea, from Dublin to Liverpool, in a balloon.*3

Back at the Commodore, Sunday evening was fully occupied contemplating all of this, in between browsing through maps, old newspapers and other ageing documents. The business over 'my' hotel left me feeling like I had had all those lovely Christmas presents snatched away from under my very nose. I retired for the night, feeling thoroughly let down.

NOTES, CHAPTER 12

*1 The terms U and non-U were devised by the author Nancy Mitford, writing in the 1950s about class distinctions and the English aristocracy. Lucie - at least, on her own estimation - would have been a very definite U person!

*2 That situation was rectified in the summer of 1994, when visitors from the Titanic Historical Society - based in Massachusetts, USA - included Cobh in their tour of the British Isles. A report of their visit appears in the White Star Journal, Vol.2. No.2.

*3 Whale, Derek: Lost Villages of Liverpool, Part Two, Stephensons (1984), p. 11.

Chapter 13

Nothing ever seems so bad in the morning. Awakened by the dawn chorus, I began to count my blessings... to draw comparisons between points emerging from the regression and the known facts about the journey.

On one side of the paper, I scribbled down information which had come from hypnotic recall; on the other, the actual facts. The results, I had to admit, were impressive.

POINT ONE; the overcrowded tenders. Yes, agreed Tom Williams. With 113 passengers aboard, it would have been.

POINT TWO; On board ship, Lucie bemoaned the fact that the sleeping quarters for unmarried men and women were at opposite ends of the ship.

Geoff Whitfield confirmed that the cabins of unmarried men and women were indeed separated, as described.

POINT THREE; Reference was also made to a wailing woman dropping her rosary beads overboard. That, apparently, was also correct. A passenger named Nora Keane firmly believed the Titanic would not reach New York safely. She is known to have upset many others with constant repetition of her prediction.

According to American author and historian, George Behe, Miss Keane referred several times to her misgivings, saying 'Glory be to God. This ship will never reach New York!' Miss Keane's fear, he added, was believed to have originated when she dropped her rosary beads into the sea.*[1]

POINT FOUR; When Lucie made her sneaky visit to the First Class section she was bowled over by the sight of the magnificent dome above the grand staircase; the clock, the symbolic figures, ornate lift doors, pretty cafes and splendid dining rooms.

Cynics might discount these descriptions, because anyone who has ever seen pictures of, or films about, Titanic would know all that. Nevertheless, it was intriguing for me, as Lucie, to actually 'see' them in all their splendour.

POINT FIVE; During one of her regressions, Lucie had been irritated by the fact that many of her fellow passengers spoke no English. The same conclusion could be drawn as from point four above; it is general knowledge that there were many Scandinavian and Italian families travelling steerage. Nevertheless, seeing them in the flesh and hearing them gabbling away among themselves proved an enlightening experience.

POINT SIX; Dennie had told Lucie that the captain's name was Edward John Smith, which was why he was generally known as E.J. Lucie herself had been particularly impressed by how smart the captain and his officers looked when they carried out their daily inspections.

True on all three counts. The captain's name was Smith, he was generally town as E.J.. he did carry out a daily inspection as described .*[2]

POINT SEVEN; Lucie had also overheard talk among her fellow passengers that Captain Smith was soon to retire.

That, too, is historically accurate. Edward John Smith was 59 years old. And yes...After taking Titanic to New York for her maiden voyage and back to Southampton, he did plan to retire.*[3]

POINT EIGHT; On the Sunday morning, at the start of what was to be their last full day aboard, Lucie told Dennie about the Divine Service in the First Class Dining Saloon.

That is exactly were the Divine Service was held.*[4]

POINT NINE; Lucie, unable to sleep, was out on deck on that momentous night. Glancing overboard, she saw a large white object approach and collide with the ship. She watched the mysterious object skim along the side of the vessel, scratching and ripping, then calmly moving off into the distance as if nothing had happened.

Again, cynics would claim that everyone who was even remotely interested in the story of the tragic maiden voyage KNEW that was how it happened. But how many people are alive today who can claim that they actually saw the icy fingernails of the hand of fate scratch along the vessel, and were still there when Titanic's life's blood poured out to merge with the ocean?

Added to all that, were the numerous similarities in Cobh itself, between Lucie's observations and established facts... the hill up from the railway station; the horse drawn cab, the promenade, gardens, bandstand, gun carriage, hot dog stand and jetty, all as related in chapter eleven. . .

Over breakfast, I learned that Mrs Vicky Barry, owner of the Galley, had a stock of historic pictures. So, plucking up all of Lucie's courage as well as my own, I prepared to enter the former Emigrants' Home.

The exterior had conjured up no mental images at all, so I hardly expected to glean anything from the interior.

Lucie might have had her reasons for avoiding the place, but it made no sense whatever to me.

Once inside, I could see why.

In a flash, everything became suddenly and disconcertingly clear as the daunting truth hit me like a bolt from the blue. Talk about a home from home!

With its huge sweeping staircase, carved wooden banisters, brasswork and panelled walls, I knew this house only TOO well. And so did Lucie... despite the fact that she had been holding back on the truth for so long.

Little snob had pretended to have stayed at the Imperial, but this was where she had really hung up her hat, and her pretty little blue dress. This was where she and Dennie had stayed before setting off on their eventful trip. I KNOW she stood outside the door of the Imperial and gazed longingly at those with more cash at their disposal and I SUSPECT that she told anyone who asked that she was a guest at the hotel; but the fact remains: she never set her dainty little foot inside the place.

THIS was where she had stayed. How very illuminating: it explained my great feeling of disappointment over the lack of recognition once I had stepped inside the building next door.

With this one, the situation was reversed. I recognised every inch of it inside, and nothing at all outside. The front of the building stirred up no memories whatever. Why was that, I asked Mrs Barry?

"Because the original facade was burned down some years back," she told me. "That brickwork and those stained glass windows are modern."

Frankly gawping at the familiarity of my surroundings, I followed Mrs Barry up the broad staircase; the brass finish of each step glinting mischievously in the strong, morning sunshine. I was shown into the room where the emigrants, and later the servicemen, would have gathered.

Mrs Barry pointed to the walls, all panelled with pitch pine, and the floor boarding of thick, limestone blocks. Through a rear window, we saw an extension, where topmost windows had safety bars.

Sorrow this house doubtless felt in the past, and its share of nostalgia, too. Residents would have sung, danced and gathered around the pianola in here, she added. I knew they would. I 'remembered' the rolls of the thing revolving round and round as the odd-sounding music poured forth. But most of all, I could recall the sound of the fiddle, the pipes and the piano accordion: this latter instrument being colourfully described as 'come-to-me, go-from-me' because of the movement required to produce the music.

I could hear again the wail of the pipes that man was playing. They were bagpipes, yet they were not... I could still 'hear' his compatriots referring to them as 'ill...' something. Perhaps they were old, and ailing, I reasoned.

(As with the information about Scotts' Quay, referred to in Chapter Eleven, the explanation as to why the pipes should be so named did not come to my notice for another three years[*5]).

The property itself was actually quite beautiful. Though no longer residential, it was an amazingly classy place, with its tall ceilings and ornate fireplaces.

It occured to me that in London a home such as this would be worth a great deal of money. Apparently, before 1855, the very exclusive Cork Yacht Club was based here.

On then to my next 'port of call'.

At the headquarters of James Scott and Co., ship agents, I had a coffee with Mr Frank Taft, one of the directors. Sight of the two pictures on the wall of his office made me gulp hard. Why?

Because these were the very scenes which had lived in my mind for as long as I could remember. One was of the crowded promenade, with the ladies in their long dresses bustling about around trees which were definitely not palms, and sitting, chatting together on benches which were definitely not wooden. And there, in the centre, was the bandstand with the hood that I knew it should have had.

The second picture was of passengers boarding the tenders to take them out to Titanic. Mr Taft, like Captain Nash, showed me copies of contemporary documents: in this case relating to shipping and the need for travellers to arrive at the port two days in advance of travelling. This was a legal requirement, in order for them to obtain the necessary documentation, pass their medicals, and so on.

Tickets were priced per 'soul', not per 'head' or 'each' as we might think of them today. Through the window of his office, Mr Taft pointed to the wooden hot dog stall, confirming that it was a survivor from the period in which I was interested.

"Only at that time, it was mobile," he added. "They pulled it up and down the prom, selling tea and coffee."

Summing up my findings, I attempted to make some sense of what was hapening. It had been positively mind-blowing to discover that Dennis and Mary Lennon had actually been on board, and that both had been lost.

I knew this because, shortly before I had left for my trip to Cobh, Geoff Whitfield had updated me on what had happened in the aftermath of the tragedy.

On Wednesday, April 17, 1912, the cable steamer Mackay Bennet left Halifax, Nova Scotia, with instructions to search the area where Titanic sank for the bodies of passengers and crew. In the event, she recovered three hundred and six.

Most were male, but something about one of the females brought a lump to my throat. A week after leaving Halifax, the vessel brought its sixty third victim on board for possible identification. Details entered in the ledger listed the body as being that of a young woman in her late teens or early twenties. She was wearing a blue dress and black shoes. 'Effects: purse, with miniature photo of a young man, key, few coins, photo locket. No marks on body or clothing.'

Back at the Commodore hotel, I added POINT TEN to my list.

Lucie was wearing her favourite blue dress, with her locket around her neck. Was she really Body Number Sixty-three? If so, there was a slight discrepancy. Lucie met her fate because she spent too long looking for one of her shoes; but Body Number Sixty-three definitely appears to have had two of them. Frankly, I didn't know what to make of the discovery. I still don't. That particular piece of information sent goose pimples running along my spine, and still does, every time I think of it.

If, as Mrs Lewis claimed (Chapter Nine), the runaway girl WAS expecting a child (though Lucie herself never made reference to the possibility), the crew of the salvage vessel did not mention the fact. The records simply state that the remains were committed to the sea again on the same day (Tuesday, April 23).

Of Dennis Lennon ('Dennie') there is no trace at all. I suspect his body was never recovered from the sea. I would like to think that they died in each other's arms and that they have stayed together for eternity.

On the subject of Dennis and Mary, here's the strangest, quirkiest, co incidence of all. Those were the very names of my own parents. Was this a fluke, or did telepathy somehow travel forward for my alter ego to pick up the names of the couple who would carry her Life Force into a new generation?

In the wake of my visit to Cobh, my word processor was red hot as I hammered out details of a highly successful trip. I felt thoroughly pleased with myself. I had found the place which had once been an hotel with a domed canopy and the less savoury place next door; I had walked up the hill from the railway sttion, strolled along the promenade, ventured on to the wooden jetty, stood before the former mobile beach hut and even smelt the carbolic of the bath house. I had discovered poor dear Lucie to be something of a poseur: pretending to be staying at the Imperial Hotel, when she was really at the Emigrants' Home. It made me wonder, yet again, if her father WAS a Baron as she claimed. Having stumbled acoss one of her guilty secrets, I wondered if any more were locked away in the cupboards of her mind.

I decided there was only one avenue left for me to pursue now. I had to find her home. I simply HAD to. Oh... a final point. In a full colour painting by American artist, Ken Marschall reproduced in an illustrated history of Titanic[*6] - the sumptuous decor surrounding the grand staircase can be seen exactly as described by Lucie in her regression a year before Mr Marschall's book was published.

NOTES, CHAPTER 13

*1 Behe, George: Titanic; Psychic Forewarnings of a Tragedy, PSL (1988), p.33

*2 Eaton, John P and Charles A Haas: Titanic, Triumph and Tragedy, PSL (1986), p.113

*3 Lord, Walter: The Night Lives On, Viking (1986), p.42.

*4 Eaton, John P and Charles A Haas: Titanic, Triumph and Tragedy, PSL, p.114.

*5 White Star Journal, Vol.2, No.2 (Summer 1994) reports: 'Among the departing passengers on the morning of April 11, 1912, was a Mr Eugene Daly of Athlone, Co. Westmeath, who was an accomplished uileann piper.' Apparently, Mr Daly entertained passengers with traditional Irish airs as they made their way out on board the tender, America. He also played a mournful dirge, called Erin's Lament. Uileann, incidentally, is pronounced ill-ann.

*6 Lynch, Don: Titanic, an illustrated history, with paintings by Ken Marschall: Madison Press Books, Ontario/ Hodder and Stoughton, London (1992) grand staircase, p.51; lifts (elevators), p.52; dining saloon, p.54; cafes, pp58-59.

(Top) Third class passengers (including our eloping couple?) line up at Scott's Quay, Queenstown, ready to board their tender; (Bottom) West Beach, Queenstown (now Cobh) has not changed drastically since 1912. Both pictures from author's collection.

Second class passengers and the Press pack set off from Deepwater Quay, to Roches' Point where Titanic awaits.

Picture: The Cork Examiner.

From their vantage point at Titanic's stern, the emigrants look back nostalgically at what proves, in most cases heir last sight of home.

Picture: The Cork Examiner.

Has this man met and interviewed our romantic pair? If so, what names have they given him? What story have they told? Tom Barker (senior), Ireland's first Press photographer, is the last cameraman to take pictures on board Titanic before she sails to her doom.

Picture: The Cork Examiner.

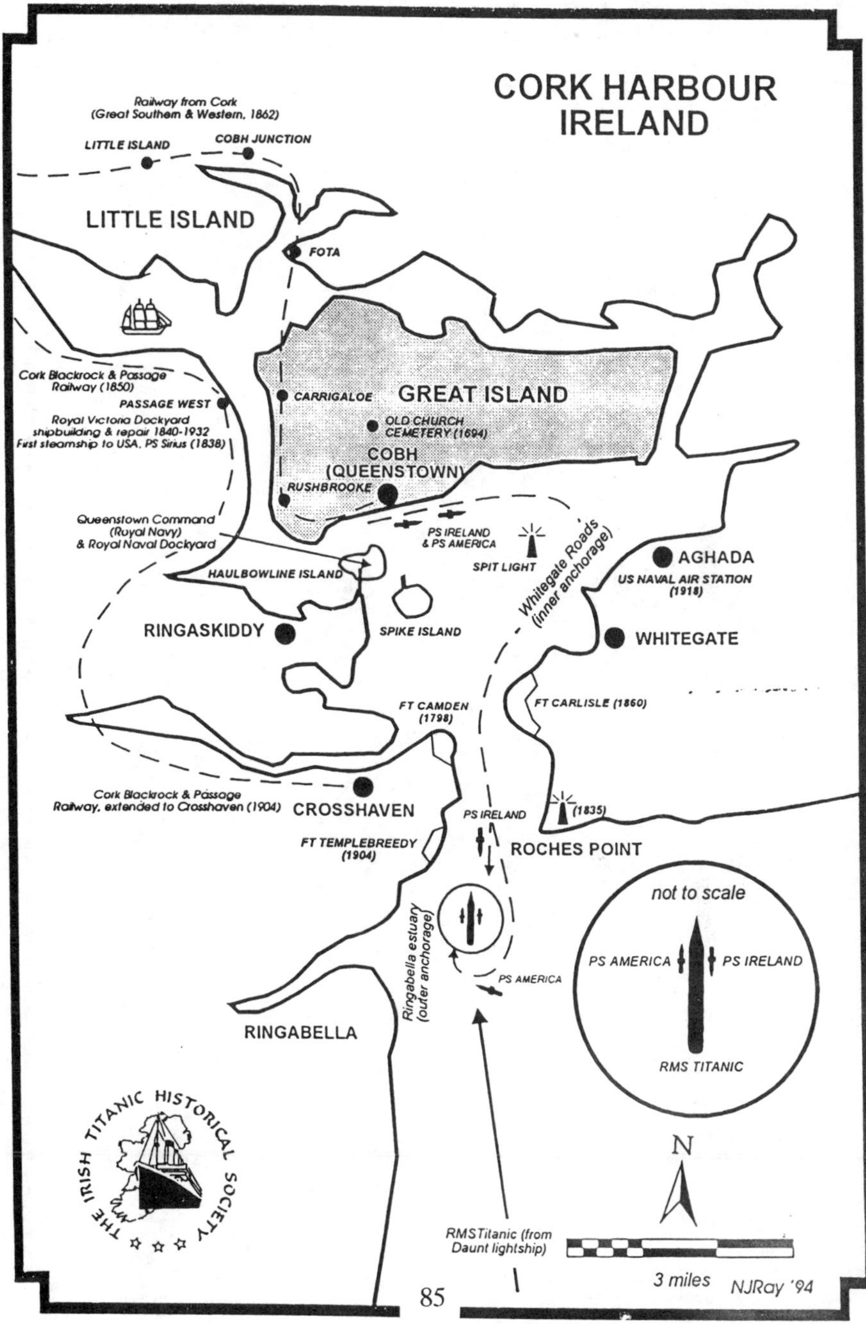
CORK HARBOUR
IRELAND
Railway from Cork
(Great Southern & Western, 1862)
LITTLE ISLAND
COBH JUNCTION
LITTLE ISLAND
FOTA
Cork Blackrock & Passage
Railway (1850)
PASSAGE WEST
Royal Victoria Dockyard
shipbuilding & repair 1840-1932
First steamship to USA, PS Sirius (1838)
CARRIGALOE
GREAT ISLAND
OLD CHURCH
CEMETERY (1694)
COBH
(QUEENSTOWN)
RUSHBROOKE
Queenstown Command
(Royal Navy)
& Royal Naval Dockyard
PS IRELAND
& PS AMERICA
SPIT LIGHT
Whitegate Roads
(inner anchorage)
AGHADA
US NAVAL AIR STATION
(1918)
HAULBOWLINE ISLAND
RINGASKIDDY
SPIKE ISLAND
WHITEGATE
FT CAMDEN
(1798)
FT CARLISLE (1860)
Cork Blackrock & Passage
Railway, extended to Crosshaven (1904)
CROSSHAVEN
PS IRELAND
(1835)
FT TEMPLEBREEDY
(1904)
ROCHES POINT
not to scale
Ringabella estuary
(outer anchorage)
PS AMERICA
PS AMERICA
PS IRELAND
RMS TITANIC
RINGABELLA
THE IRISH TITANIC HISTORICAL SOCIETY
N
RMSTitanic (from
Daunt lightship)
3 miles
NJRay '94

Map of Cork Harbour courtesy Irish Titanic Historical Society.

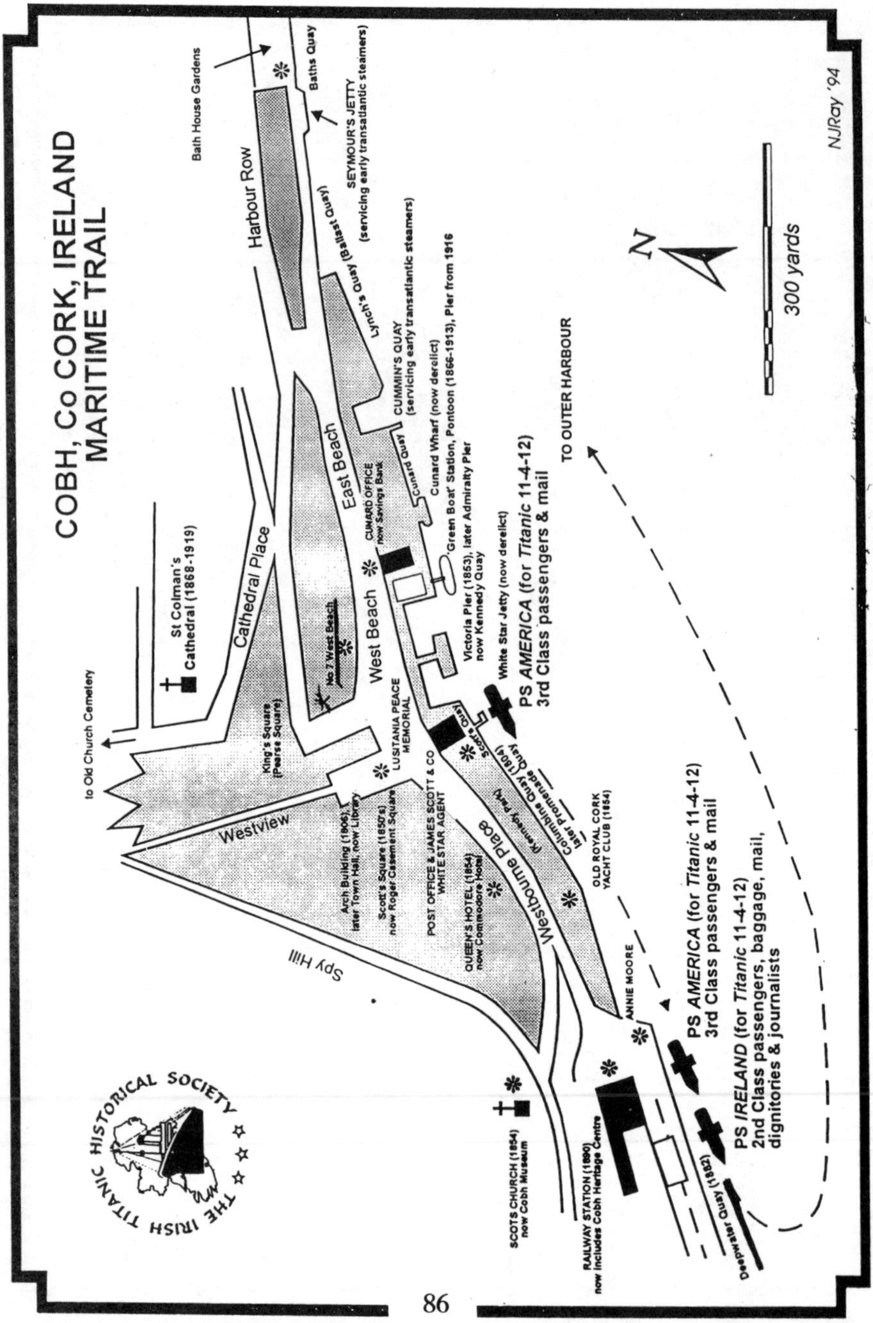

Map of Coth's Maritime Trail courtesy Irish Titanic Historical Society.

In the days of mass emigration, the Old Custom House at Queenstown was a hive of activity.
Today, the building stands deserted. Picture by the author.

PART THREE

Chapters 14 - 16

Widening the search

Chapter 14

My search for Lucie - and possibly a sister - involved writing letters to the authorities in both Devon and Cornwall. Of each, I enquired about the Latymer ladies, explaining that their father was a gentleman farmer and that the family may have lived in a large white house. A pretty hopeless quest, it might have seemed. Stupidly, I forgot to mention the railway station at the gate, which would surely have made investigations easier.

Consultation with readily available sources in the West Country Studies Library, produced nothing of note, so the area librarian suggested I contact both the Cornwall Record Office, in Truro and the Cornish Studies Library, in Redruth.

I did as suggested and found the authorities most helpful.

At Cornwall Record Office, Robert Petre, the archivist, checked the region's directories for 1902 and 1910. Frustratingly, he could find no record of Latimers in the area for the period in question.

Information provided by the Cornwall Record office was more promising. Terry Knight, principal librarian told me he had found something of interest. Kelly's directories of Cornwall for 1914 and 1919 contained entries for Misses Latimer, and gave their address as Trequite House, St Kew, Wadebridge.

Mr Knight explained that the entries were in the private residents listings and did not include everyone, having evolved from the early editions' Court Lists.

He could find no trace of Arthur Stenning,[*1] but in answer to my enquiry about how the couple might have travelled to Queenstown, he said he was not aware of any regular direct sailings from Cornwall.

"But I imagine travellers might have come to Bristol, or even made their way up to Liverpool.

"There might have been the occasional sailing by a working boat, of course."

There might, indeed. I have a distinct impression of our eloping couple enduring a none-too-comfortable crossing on one of those.

With fingers firmly crossed, I dropped a line to the occupier of Trequite House, St Kew: always assuming that the house was still standing and actually had an occupier. What, I asked, did they know about the Latimers, or Latymers? And, in passing, what was the meaning of the house's strange name? (Did Trequite equal big and white?)

The reply, which came by return of post, put me in a state of febrile tension... and anticipation. The letter was from a Mrs N.G.Routledge, who said:

"My family and I have lived at Trequite House for twenty-eight years. The previous owner, Mr T Andrews, still lives locally and has given me the following information:

"The two sisters who lived here were, in fact, half sisters. One was Miss Elizabeth (known as Bessie), the other Miss Cadman.

"Bessie Latimer was Mr Andrews' godmother.

"He is of the opinion that they had been wealthy and employed black servants."

Could one of those 'black' servants have simply been brown from his work out of doors? And could his name have been Arthur Stenning? Or was I picking up pieces from a different jigsaw and trying to force them into this one? Correction; was I picking up pieces from my jigsaw and attempting to bang them into someone else's?

Sadly, for the mood of my story, these two (half) sisters did not fit in at all. They were real pillars of the community and not the type I was searching for. Their lifestyle did not sound remotely familiar.

The real-life Latimer lady was elected into St Kew Church council on 27 February, 1920 and Mrs Routledge enclosed photocopies of a couple of pages of the Church Council Meetings, which mention Miss Latimer and prove what a worthy soul she was.

Shame! She did not seem at all the type to run off with a gypsy lover; and anyway, Lucie can't have been one of these two if the sisters were still around in the Twenties. Mrs Routledge even enclosed a photograph of the pair in middle age... smiling at me from across the decades.

Foiled again... as they might have said at the time.

In answer to my enquiry about the name Trequite, Mrs Routledge explained that it was a Cornish word: the prefix 'tre' meaning dwelling, homestead, or farm and 'quite' meaning woodland.

Ah, but wait a minute; the scent may not have gone as cold as I had thought. Was this farm, in the woods, Lucie's ancestral home? Was it a white, manor-house type property? Was it - I hardly dared think - the house of my dreams?

I wrote back to Mrs Routledge, this time asking her many questions. Had anyone thereabouts ever heard of Latimers (Latymers?) living in the vicinity earlier than the two sisters; had they come across an Arthur Stenning, by any chance? Was Trequite a white Georgian-type manor house?

No-one could come up with any hard evidence about my elusive family having lived there before the dates in question: though, by the same token, there was no evidence to prove that they had NOT.

Nor could Arthur Stenning be traced; but Stenning was an old Cornish name and Tintagel - the historic seat of King Arthur - was only a few miles away from St Kew. Straight up the Atlantic Highway, actually. So, wherever the labourer might have been born, both his Christian and surname were Cornish.

It was now mid-1991: five months after I had been to Cobh, and I had an uncanny feeling that the time was ripe for another lucky break. Sure enough, Lady Luck (if not exactly Lady Lucie) suddenly emerged from nowhere.

Trequite was not the house I was searching for, but I was getting warm. Mrs Routledge's next letter contained the most exciting piece of information to date.

The white house answering my description was there, all right. It was known as Lanarth, and was now a licenced hotel. Even more exciting, the Latimer sisters lived in it before moving to Trequite House.

So what on earth was going on?

A big white house, like I had dreamed of: occupied by a family of Latimers (albeit with a different spelling) but in the wrong period.

My alter-ego had long gone by the time those worthy ladies lived at Lanarth. I was almost on to Lucie ... but not quite. The scent, so strong a moment ago, was wafting away again. It was all very beguiling. The little lady was thoroughly enjoying her game of hide and seek. Or, with such incessant taunting and teasing, was it more cat and mouse?

The Cornish people are Celts. If Lucie were truly Cornish, maybe that was why she wanted to take her gypsy to Ireland and board the great liner from there.

The second possibility was that it was Stennie's yearning to meet fellow Celts that resulted in their decision to embark from the Irish port.

The third possibility was that it was all conjecture, and I was in danger of letting my imagination run riot.

Whoever made the decision, it had become abundantly clear when I was in Cobh, that Lucie had a deep affinity with Ireland and felt a happiness at Queenstown that she had never experienced anywhere else in her relatively short life.

If Lucie did travel on Titanic, and the evidence does seem to point that way, two pertinent questions arise. Firstly, how would they have travelled to Queenstown? Secondly, why would they have chosen to go there, rather than to Southampton like all the other English passengers?

How?

Well, it has already been established that, with the massive British Army presence in Ireland at the time, much of the traffic plying to and fro, would be heading for Queenstown.

In addition to routine service and passenger sailings, cattle ships constantly travelled from various English and Welsh ports; and what captain would not be happy to oblige a young couple on the run, if the money was right?

Why?

Perhaps they wanted to set a false trail. Then again, if Stennie had friends in the labouring or gardening communities, they may well have been able to fix a free passage for two on a cattle steamer, or some such mode of transport.

When and where 'Stennie' became 'Dennie' was still anyone's guess. As yet, I couldn't even begin to work that one out.

The runaways would have been made aware of the need to stay in port for at least forty-eight hours before sailing, in order to obtain the necessary documentation.

To stay in Southampton for the required period may have been considered too risky; they may have assumed, rightly as it happened, that they would stand a better chance of 'losing' themselves in the remote Irish countryside.

Also, if they did plan to marry, they would need to cover their tracks somewhere far removed from the family home: not just in a different county, but in a different country.

Lucie must have known that her father would never think of searching for her in Ireland. So she probably felt relatively safe in and around Queenstown. How very providential that the Cork Spring Show should have been taking place on the very week of the sailing; making it even easier for our runaways to merge, un-noticed into the crowds.

My letter to Lanarth was sent off post-haste. I wanted to go there, to see the place, to walk around the grounds, to soak up the atmosphere and find out if anything... anything at all... would be familiar.

I wanted to go immedately; without another minute's delay... but several more months were to pass before that trip became possible.

Pressure of journalistic duties and the fact that my original letter to Lanarth went astray in the post meant that I had no option but to be patient.

NOTE, CHAPTER 14

*1 Absence from the records does not necessarily prove Arthur Stenning's non-existence. Being a servant, and therefore of 'the lower order', he might not have been sufficiently literate to have entered his name on the electoral register. Or he simply might not have been sufficiently permanent in any one place to attract the attention of the authorities.

Chapter 15

Another regression to Lucie seemed like a good idea.

Perhaps she would provide some more information.. bring out the odd extra clue that would prove beyond a shadow of doubt that she DID live in Lanarth, that her father WAS a baron, that her mother HAD drowned, albeit in less dramatic circumstances than those under which she herself had been lost.

On the evening of Saturday, June 22, 1991, I was regressed again; this time in the presence of Geoff Whitfield, the BTS Honorary Secretary, his wife Alma; Michael and Sharon Bott, a couple of actor friends visiting from London; and my son Arthur, who had travelled from Kent for the weekend.

Armed with all the information gleaned to date, the assembled group felt that perhaps on this occasion a few leading questions might be in order.

Normally, such questions are totally off the agenda; but in Lucie's case, because she was such an awkward character and would not answer like everyone else, the questions would now be presented in a way that would test her attitude and body language. And they would be put to her not only by Joe, but by other members of the group.

How, in the character of Lucie, would I react?

Lucie's behaviour and her responses were not something I could ever predict.

Nor could I say in advance how she might react towards those who were about to question her. (In the event, it was appalling and I had to apologise most profusely to my friends for her attitude and behaviour. The way Lucie spoke to them was inexcusable... of which, more anon).

All I knew for sure was that information which my conscious mind did not have, was always freely available to my subconscious. By the same token, although consciously I knew full well it was my husband who normally questioned me, my subconscious mind, under regression, regarded him simply as The Voice.

I was aware, too, that present-day facts were shrouded in mist and out of the regressed character's reach because, back in that period, the associated events had not yet happened.

My perception of images was rather different.

Always, under regression, it was as if a colour print had been superimposed on a much sharper black and white one; or, to use another analogy, as if I were at one and the same time watching, and taking part in a film. Never, at any stage, was I totally oblivious to my environment.

Images of the past knitted in with those of the present, to achieve a fascinating end result; but I had no great difficulty with that. Recollections of Lucie's life seemed no more strange and no less sharp than recollections of my own childhood. The recalled events occured earlier: there was no more to it than that.

During this latest regression, as with all the others, I knew I was at home on Merseyside, surrounded by my husband and friends; but I was also way back there in the early days of the century, with an amorous gypsy. (Thankfully, I have a most understanding husband!)

What regression did prove to me quite forcibly though, was that the subconscious mind was mighty powerful, and would always sublimate the conscious... particularly when it came to distant recall.

Consciously, I knew that a girl called Eleanor Truelove Latimer had run away with her lover, that she had a sister called Alice and a maid called Sarah Jane yet, in regression, the names Eleanor Truelove and Alice meant nothing to me, though the name Sarah Jane did stir up something vague. There was no reaction whatever to the place names, Probus and Southampton (which had also been referred to by Mrs Lewis when she spoke of Eleanor's disappearance). . .

What was it that attracted Stennie (Dennie... or whoever he was) to Lucie? I still can't fathom how he put up with her, because she came through as the most smug, self-satisfied, self-opinionated little bitch I had ever encountered. An arch snob. Truly obnoxious.

I hope I was not quite that bad at her age, but I can safely state that Lucie had different emotional and psychological characteristics from mine. Where she longed for company as a child, I preferred to be alone. Where she was arrogant and super-confident, I was a shy, introverted little thing. Timidity personified.

She hated her father and looked down her haughty nose at the governess: I worshipped my father, didn't have a governess, but during my formative years, our housekeeper was my best friend. She found her piano lessons tedious, I loved mine.

Where she was quite the competent little needlewoman, I have no interest in sewing. Her childhood domestic pets were dogs, mine were cats.

But there were similarities, too... we share a certain awkward streak of nature, a love of plants, flowers, pretty shoes, an enchantment with the place she knew as Queenstown and I, as Cobh; and we both have music in our souls.

Could that love of music be responsible for the strangely evocative mood that comes over me when I hear gypsy tunes? (I shall refrain from enlarging upon how I feel when I set eyes on gorgeous black-eyed, curly-haired gypsies in THIS life!).

Is it possible for feelings, words, sentiments to hang over from one life to the next? If these regressions really are evidence of past-life recall, then it would certainly seem to be the case.

Anyway, here I was, as before, being induced into the deepest form of hypnosis and guided back gently to April, 1912.

Once more, I found myself on that busy promenade, gazing longingly at the hotel overlooking the jetty.

"Where are you, Lucie?"

I felt my nose turn up of its own accord before I responded, with the usual cut glass speech.

"I am here."

"Where is here, Lucie? Can you describe the place?"

"It is beautiful. Quite, quite beautiful..."

"Is it by the sea?"

"Of COURSE it is by the sea." The feeling was, as before, one of intense irritation. Couldn't The Voice SEE where she was?

While one half of my mind appeared to belong to Lucie, the other half was definitely my own, because at that point, I was still fully aware of the whispering voices around me; aware that one of them belonged to Geoff, who was explaining to the others that, at the time, liners and cargo vessels were berthing and sailing almost as frequently as the tides themselves. As a result of this information, one of the group sitting around me asked:

"Can you see any ships, Lucie?"

And once more dear Lucie shook her head in amazement. How could she possibly see any ships when she was, at this precise moment, standing with her back to the promenade; gazing instead at the impressive entrance of the hotel with the extended canopy. She was fascinated by the sight of all the smartly-dressed ladies and gentlemen coming and going with their gentlemen escorts carrying suitcases and valises.

How many of them, she wondered, would be travelling on the big ship with herself and her love? She heard The Voice address her again, but not being in the habit of answering silly questions, she remained silent. Then it said:

"Lucie...I would like to introduce you to a lady called Alma..."

"How do you do," retorted Lucie, stiffly. One must, after all, remember one's manners.

"Hello, Lucie," the stranger greeted her in an accent she had never heard before. Where on earth had this person come from?

"And this is Sharon," The Voice went on.

Lucie nodded. Sharon said

"Good morning..."

"It is AFTERNOON.." snapped Lucie.

"Oh, I do apologise," responded this second female voice in a voice whose tone gave Lucie to understand the lady was laughing behind her handkerchief. How very rude. The unseen person said suddenly: "Meet my husband, Michael."

"How do you do?" The man's tone was polite.

His voice reminded her of an occasion when Papa had had a visitor from London. Perhaps he came from there, too. Lucie's ear had always been well attuned to people's voices.

A few, she liked. Most, she despised. It was people's voices which decided, more than anything else, whether they were worth speaking to, or not.

"And here's Arthur..."

Lucie bridled. Arthur was NOT here: and how could anyone possibly have known about Stennie's real name being Arthur? What else did they know?

Had someone told them about Dennie?

The very thought of others knowing her secret brought on an attack of the vapours. This was very worrying. Very worrying, indeed. The sooner they were on the big ship, the safer they would be.

At that point, I felt Lucie's mind and my own coalesce in a way they had never done before. It was the most disturbing experience I had ever had during the course of my many regressions.

The shock of hearing that name was almost enough to bring me out of regression and out of hypnosis altogether,

"Off to sleep, Lucie. Drift off to sleep." The Voice was calming, but it had an urgent ring that commanded instant obedience. "Now I want you to drift forward twelve hours...." I felt myself drifting, drifting, until I was curled up, half asleep, in a lumpy and most uncomfortable bed. "Are you on the ship yet?"

"No. I am not."

"Where are you then?"

"I am in bed... trying to sleep... do you MIND?"

"Where are you staying, Lucie?"

Did The Voice REALLY think she would answer that question? Lucie did not even like to admit to herself where she was staying.

The shame of it. Sharing a room with all those awful people... snoring, coughing, and making perfectly disgusting noises. And the smell of those foreigners. Didn't they EVER wash?

How very different it would have been had she been able to afford private rooms for Dennie and herself next door.

The name of Grace O'Brien filtered to her ears, and she placed her hands over them, to shut it out. She pulled the blankets up around her head, not having any desire to think of the fat, loud-mouthed woman and the greasy food she had placed on the table for dinner last evening.

That woman was even more revolting than Lucie's governess back home; nasty old crone, with ideas far above her station. At least, the governess PRETENDED to be a lady; though REAL ladies, like Lucie, knew that her acquired speech would always give her away.

Grace O'Brien, indeed. Lucie had never heard such a stupid name. Nor had she ever seen such a repulsive set of teeth. What with those big flabby arms, the hands with their grimy, bitten fingernails and the huge, fat stomach, the woman really was revolting. She had the loudest, most common laugh it had ever been Lucie's misfortune to hear. Awful, she was. A perfectly ghastly woman. Lucie had gone to bed early to get away from the landlady of this establishment and her equally vulgar cronies. The Voice must know that she hated having to associate with these people.

Why ever did anyone want to mention the fat woman's name just as Lucie's thoughts had been dwelling upon the infinitely more pleasant prospect of how lovely her future would be when shared only with Dennie?

The voice belonging to the person called Alma addressed her again, asking her all sorts of stupid questions about this place where she was staying, who the other guests (guests? ha!) were, what their sleeping and dining arrangements were and what they were being given to eat.

This really was TOO much.

"What is it to YOU?" she stormed at length; incensed that anyone should be so personal. Particularly someone who was not giving her the respect she deserved. She was just about to say so when:

"Drift off to sleep, Lucie..." ordered The Voice. She was more than happy to oblige.

Next time she heard it, she was on board ship, sitting quietly in the room they called the lounge. Dennie was organising refreshments.

The Voice introduced her to a man whose name she did not quite catch because of the row being made by some horrid foreign children screaming and fighting.

The man began asking a string of questions about the ship itself: where she slept, the colour of the towels in the cabin, where she ate, the shape of the plates and if the cups carried any emblems.

Lucie was not happy about answering this person. She condescended to do so only because she wanted him to go away, but he would not oblige. On and on, he continued to ask his question until her hackles were really raised. There was no need for all these questions and she told him so.

"I'm sorry," he said "But my eyesight is not too good. I cannot see as well as you.."

"Then it is I who should apologise," responded Lucie, suddenly remembering her manners. "What is it you wish to know? I shall do my best to answer."

"Have you noticed the colour the walls of the dining saloon?"

"They are white," she told the half-blind stranger.

"And what about those in the general room... are they the same colour?"

"No. They are made of wood."

"Ah, thank you. Then that should help me know where I am going," said he. "Tell me, are there any pictures on the walls of the general room?"

"Yes, there are several, set into the wood panels."

"Are they pretty pictures?"

"I'm afraid I don't know. I have not examined them closely."

The man continued to question her about the rooms and her cabin, until it all became tedious. He went on and on, until her patience was sorely tried. What was this room... were was that room, until, despite herself, her hackles were raised. Was there any real need for such probing, she asked the man; haughtily dismissing him as a nuisance; threatening to report him to the captain if he didn't go away.

In response, the man had the audacity to address her in a most outrageous manner:

"Real little bitch, aren't you?"

This really WAS too much. The insolence of the man. He would not get away with THAT.

Unsure of the procedure to air her grievances, she was just about to attract the attention of one of the officers, when The Voice stopped her in her tracks.

"Drift off to sleep, Lucie.. Now I want you to start coming back. Come back as Monica, but keep Lucie's attitude," came the strange suggestion.

Aroused from hypnosis, I opened my eyes, and heard my husband ask: "Well?"

"Well, WHAT?" I retorted imperiously.

Before progressing further, I should point out that, in this life, my husband and I both love animals: particularly mongrel and cross-breed dogs; having given homes to a variety of rescue mutts over the years.

But that evening, sitting there, aroused from hypnosis (though still in the persona of Lucie), I could feel that my leanings were more towards canines with impeccable pedigrees. Like myself.

"Look at Gusto!" observed one of the group, seeing my little black mongrel curl up at my feet.

I felt myself cringe:

"Yuk... a MONGREL...." I observed dismissively, and was about to express my horror at such a shaggy-looking creature being allowed into the house, when it was suggested that I call my dog to me.

"Gusto's her name," one of the group felt it necessary to explain.

"GUSTO?" I heard myself shriek.

The tone of voice was reminiscent of Lady Bracknell, with her oft-quoted 'handbag' comment.[*1]

The little animal cowered away from me, ears pinned back, tail between her legs, as she sidled towards my husband. He stroked her lovingly and, before she was caused any more distress, decided to call a halt to that particular experiment.

Gusto was not the only one confused.

One part of me was deeply upset that my beloved canine companion, who loved me intensely and who stuck to me like glue, did not want to know me. I love that dog and wanted to cuddle her, but I could not: again, proving the point about the unconscious part of the mind being stronger than the conscious.

The whole episode cannot have lasted more than a minute (two at the most), yet it felt like an eternity to me: as I've no doubt it did to my dog.

"Deep sleep... deeper and deeper. You no longer have Lucie's attitude to life. It is 1991. You are Monica. Lucie is someone else... five, four, three, two, one. WIDE awake... How do you feel now?"

"Much better, thank you," I replied, before seeking out my little friend, and inviting her to come back to me. "Come on, Gusto... good dog.... over here..."

She responded immediately, by sitting up; eyes alert, tail wagging. Then she bounded across the room, jumped all over me and covered my face with affectionate canine kisses.

I spent the rest of that evening apologising to Joe and to Gusto for the way I had spoken and reacted to them both.

"Don't be silly... that wasn't YOU...," Joe insisted.

And Lucie's behaviour towards my friends filled me with remorse. Would Geoff and Alma ever forgive me for letting Lucie act in such a disgraceful way towards them?

Far from being offended, they were enthralled. To prove that they had not taken it as a personal affront, they both agreed that there was nothing they would enjoy more than another regression session, and another opportunity to interrogate Lady Lucie.

Thankfully we were (and are) still friends.

Alma made a comment to the effect that if the spoilt, pampered little lady had gone on much longer, she (Alma) would have been sorely tempted to smack her. I had to agree that Lucie's behaviour was reprehensible. No true lady would ever address anyone in such a high-handed manner.

Geoff was intrigued to think that the character to whom he had been speaking might have actually been on board the stricken liner.

"But if she was really like that, she didn't fall overboard; she was probably pushed," he quipped.. "If I'd been around at the time, I'd have pushed her myself."

Perhaps he was... and he did!

The observations of Sharon and Michael were that, if this was acting, I was pursuing the wrong career.

And Arthur (my son)? For once in his life, he was totally dumbstruck.

NOTE, CHAPTER 15

*1 Wilde, Oscar: The Importance of Being Earnest (1895). The formidable dowager, Lady Augusta Bracknell, on hearing that Ernest had lost both parents, been 'mislaid' as a baby, then found at Victoria Station, scornfully repeated the young man's own words with her memorable observation: 'in a HANDBAG?'

Chapter 16

John P. (Jack) Eaton and Charles Haas are highly-esteemed Titanic historians, authors and founders of the society known as Titanic International. They live in America, but visit Great Britain from time to time for research purposes.

The latest joint venture - on the hospital ship, Britannic,[1] sister of Titanic - brought them to Merseyside in mid-July, 1991. We were delighted to welcome them to our home on the evening of Wednesday, the 24th. And yes... Geoff and Alma Whitfield came too. They fancied the idea of Jack and Charles meeting Lucie and, if possible, questioning her. Regression was something of which neither of the American authors had any previous knowledge.

Lucie, as ever, was on form. Haughty, imperious and impossible; she was still turning up her nose at the questions being asked: still being a thorough pain in the neck.

The American accents of Jack and Charles upset her even more than the local tones of Geoff and Alma. She told them, in no uncertain terms, what she thought of them and their nosiness. Once more, apologies were called for and laughingly dismissed.

For me at the receiving end of whatever Lucie felt like beaming out, it was all very real. Taken to the death scene, I felt again that intense terror that, even in the memory, combined to make my teeth chatter and my whole body tremble.

I relived the anguish of my alter-ego as the rising waters reached her ankles, knees, waist and chin. Once more, I felt myself gulping and gasping for breath, before being catapulted into darkness.

The American authors appeared somewhat flabbergasted to be speaking, apparently through time, to someone whose mind appeared to have been back in the very period of history which they had spent most of their professional lives researching.

Again, during the course of being returned to the present and before being aroused from hypnosis, Joe - as is his custom - instructed me to retain all of Lucie's memories, except the pain and the emotions.

Questioned by our American guests about various aspects of life on board, I came up with answers that seemed to satisfy them about the authenticity of the regression; though they could not quite get their heads around the concept of my being aboard Titanic. After all, there was no record of 'me' or 'my man' on their comprehensive passenger lists.

They were, of course, very familiar with the names of Mary and Dennis Lennon; but then, those names never actually came out in regression, which is hardly surprising given the circumstances.

Having checked his records, Jack informed us that the couple had travelled jointly on ticket number 370371. The young woman's age was given as twenty, her partner's as twenty-one; but he could not provide an address for either, and had only the most elementary personal details:

"She is described as a spinster and he as a general labourer," he said, adding that the ticket cost them £15 sterling "It appears to be entered on the ticketing list quite close to the bottom, as though it were a late purchase... but we can't be certain of this."

He added that they were apparently travelling as brother and sister.

It all sounded very plausible.

Lucie was a cocky little madam and WOULD have passed for twenty. She WAS a spinster, though it was not a term she would have been likely to have used herself. But then, she could hardly have admitted to being a Lady, or an Honorable, could she?

And they WERE travelling as brother and sister. I can vouch for that...

While we, in England, were pondering the imponderable, across the Irish Sea, Tom Williams was doing his own spot of ghost-hunting: still ploughing through sheafs of yellowing documents in search of anything significant. He sat up into the small hours delving deep into the background of all those who had embarked at Queenstown, but long since crossed the Great Divide.

Wading through the mass of information accumulated in the months since we had started our investigations he, like the American authors, also had documented evidence about every one of those travellers. And sure enough, missing from his list too, was the address of the couple whose identity had been suspect from the start: Dennis and Mary Lennon.

But he had something else.

"I have tracked down the story of a runaway couple who left Queenstown on Titanic," he told me in an excited phone call. "According to contemporary newspaper reports, at least one of them used a false name and the girl was said to have been turned away from the parental home because the lover was not considered good enough for her.

"Both were believed to have been in their early twenties (though could have been younger) and the girl is reported to have been a member of the landed gentry. Both were lost."

It was, he enthused, generally believed that this was the couple who called themselves Dennis and Mary Lennon.

Reports of the runaway couple's plight appeared in the Cork Examiner, of April 17, 1912 and in the Daily Mirror on the following day. Each referred to a well-connected girl aged about twenty, who was turned away from the parental home.

The news reports explained that both were travelling under false names, that they were seen in the tender leaving Queenstown and spoken to when aboard the ill-fated vessel,

To eliminate the possibility that they might have secretly married before they set off on their epic journey, Tom approached the archives department at St Colman's Cathedral, Cobh, to ask if there were any records of a marriage certificate of either Arthur Stenning and Lucie Latymer or Dennis and Mary Lennon (nee Latymer).

The cathedral administrator informed him that he could find no records of either set of names. If the couple had married in any (Catholic) church in the county of Cork; this was where it would have been recorded.

The fact that they were probably not Catholic quite eluded Tom. Me too, for that matter but, by then, we had both decided that there was no point in pursuing that angle any further.

As far as I was concerned, although the couple travelling in the names of Dennis and Mary Lennon had intended marrying, they had not yet tied the knot, which was why they had to settle for travelling as brother and sister.

So were the couple anonymously referred to in those press reports really Lucie and Stennie (alias Dennie), or a different couple altogether? Tom, still with the bit between his teeth, was determined to try another line of enquiry.

"I'm hoping that the manager of the railway station might be able to shed some light on the subject," he remarked. "I know that the simple act of buying a railway ticket could not possibly give any idea of the identity of the purchaser. But the fact that the entire train was probably chartered by the White Star Line suggests that they would have kept a positive record of everyone booked on the boat train and also on the liner."

I was not so sure. That was 1912, after all. To coin a phrase, much water had passed under (or, in this case, over) the bridge since then.

I was not at all surprised when he came back with the disappointing news that he had been unable to obtain the necessary passenger list from the railway's files. . .

But all was not lost. In the same post I had received a letter from Lanarth. Yes, the hotel had some vacancies and could accommodate me as soon as I wished. A telephone booking was made and I arranged to travel down there the following week.

I went out, straight away, purchased my railway ticket, and prepared myself to take some more 'footsteps on the sands of time'.*2

NOTES, CHAPTER 16

*1 Britannic was sunk by enemy action in the Aegean Sea, in 1916.

*2 Longfellow, Henry W: A Psalm of Life.

PART FOUR

Chapters 17 - 21

CORNWALL

Chapter 17

Travelling, via public transport, from the Wirral penninsula to a remote village in North Cornwall was no easy task. I had left my Wirral home at nine in the morning, had to change trains at Liverpool, Crewe and Birmingham, before arriving at Bodmin Park a full nine hours later.

A bus was supposed to serve the route from Bodmin Park to Wadebridge; from where, according to the helpful people at British Rail enquiries, I should have no difficulty finding a taxi to take me the remaining five miles to St. Kew Highway.

However, in the way of such matters, my train was running thirty minutes late. The bus failed to turn up, station staff had finished for the day and there was no-one around to ask what happened next. There was no-one around. Full stop.

Here I was, on the edge of Bodmin Moor on a cold, wet evening in mid-October. The rain was now coming down in torrents and the only place to shelter was in the phone box. Thankfully, a taxi firm's card was stuck to the wall, so I called them out. It was another thirty minutes before my vehicle arrived.

I began to feel I was on a wild goose chase and that Someone Up There was having a good laugh at my expense. So much for the railway station supposed to be sited at the very gate of Lucie's home: if indeed, the place I was struggling so hard to reach ever did have a railway station or, for that matter, had ever housed the young runaway for whom I was searching.

Surely, of all the stupid things I had done in my day, this trip to Cornwall topped the list. What on earth was I doing out in the middle of nowhere, heading for a house I believed to have once been occupied by a character who may never have existed?

The taxi arrived. We covered a good twenty miles and as, by now, darkness had really set in, I recognised nothing. We passed through Wadebridge and continued our journey along the A39.

The name of Lanarth was not one with which the driver was familiar, though he did have a rough idea of the location of St Kew Highway. I was, I informed him, looking for a large white Georgian-type manor house in several acres of grournd: approached by a wide entrance and a long driveway. There should be a railway station at the gate, I added hopefully.

He cheerfully admitted that he seldom ventured this side of Bodmin, but could state categorically that there was no railway station around here. There wasn't even one at Wadebridge, he reminded me, which was why he had to collect me at Bodmin Park. Yes, I agreed; but had there ever been one here?

He didn't know. He had not been taxi-ing for long, he added in a friendly, but not altogether helpful manner. So it was I who first noticed the sign saying Lanarth Inn and Caravan Park.. suppressing the urge to say what Papa would have thought of THAT.

I indicated to the driver that this was where I was heading. We pulled off the road, and turned right into a long, winding driveway; at the end of which, I was duly deposited at the door of the bar. I paid him, thanked him, entered the place and ordered a stiff drink... cursing inwardly, because there was nothing remotely familiar about this watering hole. Nothing at all.

The bar was modern and full of noisy local people making merry. Men, mostly. It appeared to be a popular meeting place for the dart-playing community if the many shields and trophies were anything to go by. For the second time that evening, I thought of how Papa would disapprove. HE seemed to be hovering about the place pretty strongly, even if dear Lucie was nowhere to be found. It was a most unsettling presence.

I hoped I wasn't going to bump into the spectre of His Lordship and be sternly reprimanded for the misdeeds of his errant daughter. The very thought was enough to make me order another drink... but, this time, I made it non-alcoholic. Writers, like policemen, should never drink on duty.

Warmed and replenished, I wandered through the door leading to the main part of the hotel and stopped short. I was gripped by the sort of feeling I can only describe as something akin to deja-vu: the phenomenon where you feel you have been there before, but know you haven't.

The difference between what I was experiencing and actual deja-vu was that I knew I HAD been here before. There was no doubt at all in my mind that this was Papa's house; the house that had failed to hold his daughter in 1912; but whose sheer magnetism had brought her back in a different form in 1991.

My eyes panned round the spacious ball and all those sturdy doors leading off it. I took in the lovely, sweeping staircase and the gracious windows. I could hardly believe the evidence of my eyes. This beautiful old house was all too, too familiar.

Approaching the discreet little desk marked reception, I tinkled the bell and a gorgeous dog bounded forward to give the sort of affectionate greeting that only dogs can.

"Brindley?" I gasped.

"Digger, actually!" corrected his mistress, who suddenly appeared from nowhere. "Sorry. He's a bit boisterous."

Shirley Keen introduced herself, checked me in and led me up those lovely stairs to a large room at the front of the property. En route there, I noticed a door on the opposite side of the corridor. It was ajar, and (rudely, now I come to think about it) I peeked inside.

"You can have that one if you prefer," suggested Mrs Keen.

"No, no. I'll be fine where I am, thank you," I managed.

My room at the front did not bring any strong memories to the fore. If Lucie had ever been in here, it had left little impression on the subconscious mind we appeared to share.

"Perhaps I could just have a little look at the other room?" I suggested.

Mrs Keen led me to it, explaining that the bed was not made up but would only take a few minutes, if it suited me better. It didn't. Not really. It only had shower facilities and, after that horrendous journey, I felt in need of a long, luxurious bath. Or that was the reasoning of my conscious mind.

My subconscious was reacting differently. Far distant memories began pushing into the forefront of my mind and their presence made me hold my breath. That room had something: and I don't just mean its atmosphere.

My attention was rivetted by the sight of the window seat: and I knew instinctively it was the very seat upon which Lucie had rested her dainty little bottom: the one on which she had spent so much of her time.

It was on this seat she had passed her dreamy hours, pretending to perfect her needlework, when in fact she was gazing out at the garden: or, more specifically, at who was working IN the garden. Without even being told, I knew that this window faced southwards, knew too that it was through here that Lucie had looked upon the face, and the delectable body, of her love. It was from this room that she had fled in haste to meet that love on an April evening many moons ago.

To sleep in this room again would be a novel idea, but I could not do it... any more than I could have slept in the childhood bedroom of the family house in Ireland when I returned there some years earlier. On that occasion, my sister and I had called in on the owners of our former home in County Cavan. They remembered us, greeted us with the sort of welcome our late parents might have given us. They would be enchanted to have us dine with them, and stay the night: in our old rooms, of course.

We thanked them kindly, but declined. We were children then, adults now. The house had grown and developed since we had lived in it. So had we. The circumstances were different. Our parents were no longer there, so WE had no place there any more, either. Trying to recapture the past in that way didn't seem right, somehow.

Yet, wasn't I trying to do the same at Lanarth?

No, I didn't think I was, actually.

I, Monica, had never lived at Lanarth: never even visited it. This trip to Cornwall was a voyage of exploration, just as surely as my trip to Cork had been. It was an exciting new 'hands-on' method of discovering how people had lived in the past: a modern version of learning history.

In that respect, it was a totally different concept from sleeping in my own childhood bedroom. At least, that was how I saw it. Others might interpret it differently.

Before retiring for the night, I told Mrs Keen I had dreamed about this house on many occasions and planned to write a book about a girl who had once lived here, had run away with a gypsy gardener employed by her father and that the girl, at least, had been lost on the Titanic. At that time, my idea was to write it in the form of a novel and call it Lady of Lanarth. "What was the lady's name?" asked Mrs Keen, intrigued. "Lucie Latymer... and her father was a baron, I believe." Mrs Keen was not familiar with the name, but then she admitted, she had only lived in Cornwall for a few years. She did, however, have deeds and documents relating to the property, dating back to 1809. She would be happy to show them to me in the morning.

Chapter 18

In the morning, the crowing of a noisy cock awakened me.

Refreshed from my night's sleep, I wandered down to the dining room; again, to be greeted by the feelings of familiarity hitting me like ping-pong balls. Coming, going, coming again; each time with a little more force than before.

The dining room had previously been the drawing room. I recognised it immediately; but where were the tall french windows leading out to the garden?

Yes, yes... they was still there, I discovered, but now hidden behind a wall which had not been there in Papa's day. The wall separated the dining room from a little room where staff of what was now an 11-bedroomed hotel relaxed and watched television.

The peacocks were still there, too; this newest generation of them strutting proudly outside the window, and looking imploringly at my breakfast. The food was first rate but I was too excited to eat very much. I reminded Mrs Keen about her promise to bring in the old map and deeds of the house.

The table was cleared, polished and I was in a state of febrile tension as she unfolded, unrolled and spread out the ageing papers. I studied land certificate, maps and a variety of documents relating to the house and district. They showed the original property on the site to have been a sixteenth century stone cottage. It was built with a well in the kitchen, but had never had a wine cellar: or not that Mrs Keen knew of.

At the time of this house's construction, Cornwall was experiencing a boom in the fishing industry and fish cellars were an integral part of many local properties. Lanarth had an adequately-sized cellar.

I wondered whether Lucie's father had managed to clear away the fish and its associated smell and keep his beloved bottles down there?

"If he did, there's no trace of them any more," sighed Mrs Keen. She added that the fish cellar remained, but had been converted and updated. Today, it formed part of the hotel's kitchen.

The main section was built in 1809, for a lady called Loveday, widow of one Dr. James Read, described on the deeds of the house as a 'doctor of physic.'

Mrs Read paid six hundred pounds for the property, and named it Newton House. It stood in the parish of St. Kew and the price included 'gardens, orchards, lands, meadows, leasowes, pastures, underwoods, paths, waters and watercourses'... some twenty acres, all told.

On the demise of the widow Loveday, the property became a gentleman's residence and the gentlemen owners listed included solicitors, an army captain, various doctors (among them, a surgeon who answered to the name of T.S.Tickell.)

"It was also used as a bishop's palace at one stage," added Mrs Keen. But she could find no reference to any baron.

And the pond, or lake, somewhere quite near the house itself?

No, I was told. The grounds of Lanarth had nothing like that; though a stream did run at the back near the orchard... but a glance at the land map showed that there had, indeed, been a pond in the grounds

I had a cup of coffee half way to my mouth. I returned it to the saucer, swallowed hard, attempted to speak, but the words wouldn't come. All of a sudden, I felt myself being transported back to that far-off day when Lucie, the child, gazed in horror at the inert figure of her mother lying face down in the water.

Trembling, I lifted the cup again, had another mouthful and somehow managed to ask:

"And... and the station house down by the gate?"

"Ah... that's not part of Lanarth any more," replied Mrs Keen. "You wouldn't have noticed when you arrived in the dark last night,.. the house is still there, but it's privately owned now... Look!" she unfolded the land map and spread it on the table. The railway had been dismantled many years ago, but the station was exactly where I knew it would be and had certainly been operational during the time in question. A quick flick through the house deeds provided details of the sale transaction.

I drained my coffee cup, picked up my pen and began to scribble furiously, pen racing across pad in order not to miss a word of what I was being told.

In 1881: 'Notice to treat by North Cornwall Railway.'

In 1885: 'Reconveyance and re-assignment (endorsed): Coode, Sandys and A.N. Other.'

A.N. Other: wasn't that just typical? The Fates were turning my quest into a real obstacle course; challenging me every inch of the way and having a good old laugh in the process.

"The station house is the big property on your left: you'll see it as you go down the drive," explained Mrs Keen..

Mrs Keen's co-owners, Ken and Janette Buckley had now joined us at the table, and informed me that the house had been converted to an hotel and restaurant in the late sixties when, for a while, it was known as The Peacock. Twenty years later, it became a country house hotel.

In its day, then, this fine house had ranged from being the home of a doctor's widow to a gentleman's residence, bishop's palace, restaurant, country house hotel, to what it had become today: a lovely, welcoming place with the warmest, friendliest atmosphere I had encountered for some time.

Yet, for all its style and elegance, Lanarth could not hold its daughter. What a shame, I thought, as I dug out my notebook pencil and camera, ready to be taken on the eagerly-awaited conducted tour.

Just as I was about to do so, a telephone call from my husband raised my spirits, as it invariably does. Only this time, he had something extra special to tell me.

A letter had arrived that morning from Angela Broome, librarian at the Royal Institution of Cornwall, with the information that a Mrs Latimer had indeed lived in this very house in 1878 and 1883; though in what capacity, she did not know.

"I have been unable to find anything further about Mrs Latimer. She does not appear in the St Kew burial register 1880-1890", she added.

She enclosed a map of St Kew Highway, which clearly depicted Lanarth, as it was in 1906 and suggested I might care to try the 1881

Census for St. Kew, available in London; or wait another few years and study that for 1891.

The only other Latimer in the vicinity was a man called Isaac. Curiously enough, like myself, he was a journalist. He can't have been Lucie's father, though, because he died sometime between 1880 and 1890 and Lucie's birth was believed not to have occured until somewhere around 1890-1895.

Could he have been her grandfather? And, if so, did she inherit her creative skills from him... her imaginatiion, her ability to spin a good yarn? Was that how she came up with the idea of changing the spelling of her name and upgrading what may well have been a yeoman farmer father into a Peer of the Realm?

Angela Broome did say that the name Latimer was a most unusual one in Cornwall... even spelt with an i. . .

(Some five years later, in correspondence with David St John Thomas, the acknowledged West Country railway historian, I asked what he knew about St Kew Highway.

It was, he told me, a single line branch.

"For most of its life, it carried four passenger trains each way daily, including a coach that formed part of the Atlantic Coast Express to and from London, whose Padstow section became an entire train on summer Saturdays."

Opened to Camelford in 1892, Delabole in 1893 and on to Wadebridge in 1895, the station was closed in 1966.)

Chapter 19

The hypnotically-recalled past life memories had not let me down. All those little details were presenting themselves in an astonishingly accurate manner.

The images emerging from my subconscious (at least, those I could pinpoint) were proving that the information I had provided during regression did have some foundation after all.

Starting with Lanarth itself: it was big, white, and stood in several acres of ground, just as I had described. There WAS a railway station at the main gates, which, in Lucie's time, would have been known as St Kew Highway station. In the days before nationalisation, it was part of the old London and South West Railway, but had closed many years ago, and its track had long since been ripped up.

Nevertheless, it was good to see that the station house was still there: though now in use as a private dwelling house. Although tastefully modernised, it still retained something of its former character.

There WAS a garden pond in the grounds of Lanarth; although it had long since been filled in, for which I was grateful. I had no wish to gaze again into the waters which had claimed the life of Lucie's unfortunate mother. Staring deep into any waters was something I preferred not to make a habit of doing.

Quirky little memories like the french windows, the cellar (albeit for fish, not wine), the peacocks, and the seat in that south-facing bedroom window added to my feelings of familiarity.

I gazed admiringly, and with more than a hint of satisfaction that they were not all figments of my imagination, at the lawns and orchards, through which the peacocks continued to strut with such magnificent pride. These beautiful creatures were not in the least bothered by human or canine interruptions to their daily routine.

Having been shown around the house itself, I was taken on a tour of the grounds and now, in the morning light, could see and appreciate the extent of Lanarth's woodland. It was exactly as it had appeared in my dreams and regressions: approached by a long and colourful drive through banks of rhododendrons, camelias and hydrangeas.

At my request, Mrs Keen escorted me to the spot where, according to her map, the pond would have been. She was curious as to why it interested me so much.

"Mama fell into it," I replied, sounding dreadfully like Lucie.

"Really?" she exclaimed.

Feeling rather silly, I explained that I had had an image of a young woman lying face down, very still, on the water. But I didn't know what happened to her after that.

"Follow me," suggested Mrs Keen, who was now really in the swing of it: "There's something you might like to see." She led me to the large, walled-in garden, now literally gone to seed. "Look..." she enthused, pushing a few tall weeds out of the way. "There's a tombstone here. Do you think that's where she might have been buried?"

I didn't think so for one moment.

When she showed me the tombstone with the eerie inscription 'Corpse, 1872', I knew it couldn't possibly be the lady I knew as Mama. Whoever, or whatever it was, would have been laid to earth long, long, before the period I was researching. But who, or what did this corpse belong to? A horse, a hound, a much-loved peacock? I could offer no explanation whatever, and felt sure that Lucie could not have done, either.

(When I raised the issue with Angela Broome at the Royal Institution of Cornwall, she responded: "At the time in question, the house was occupied by an Anglican clergyman.*[1] He is hardly likely to have permitted the burial of a human body in his own backyard!" True! The identity of the occupant, I am afraid, will have to remain unknown).

Having marvelled at the tomb of the unknown body, I was led alongside a stream, over a bridge and into the orchard, with Digger, constantly at our heels. I could see now, why the dog was so named. The paws of the spaniel were what one might call hyperactive. Indeed, he himself was too. And absolutely delightful with it. Lovely colouring too: snowy white body and light brown ears.

As we ambled along through the grounds and into the orchard Digger, though he would not have known it, began to dig up memories of that other dog, long gone. My mind drifted back to the labrador who was not quite black, nor yellow, nor even chocolate brown; but a sort of mixture of all three. He was more of a brindle colour than anything else. Hence the name: Brindley. -

The dog was gun-shy and Lucie's father was going to destroy him, but she begged and pleaded for the dog be her pet. And Papa gave in. Come to think of it, the Baron can't have been such a heartless man after all.

On this, his former estate, his presence was still very strong. So, too, was Lucie's; but then Lucie had spent much of her time out here among the trees!

Having absorbed the beauty and the feel of these lovely gardens, I excused myself, returned to my room: ostensibly to catch up on my notes and refill my camera, but actually to sneak into the bedroom of my alter-ego and soak up more of its atmosphere.

I was drawn to that room like a magnet.

Sitting on that window seat, and looking out to the garden, it occured to me that I should not have been at all surprised to see that dark, curly-haired lover of Lucie staring back at me. Quite what I would have said to him if he had, I'm not at all sure.

Nevertheless, the element of Celtic mysticism was as strong here as it had been in the place once known as Queenstown. I found this house, like the county in which it stood, to be full of atmosphere, and charm. Lanarth was, after all, only about ten miles from Tintagel Castle where King Arthur was believed to have brought his knights of the Round Table... and Arthur Stenning had found his Camelot. It was only natural that some of it should rub off on me.

Back downstairs again, I had coffee with Mrs Keen, then she passed me over to Mr Buckley, who had offered to escort me on the rest of my walkabout.

Greenhouses, stables and the tithe cottage had long gone, he explained, but the potting shed remained. Would I like to see it?

"Certainly would," I assured him.

He led me to it, opened the door, and as he ushered me inside, something remarkable happened. Exquisite pleasure invaded my senses as I was wafted back eighty years to the memory of two young lovers having a glorious time. This was the place where magic and mystery had merged.

Memories of Lucie and her love were more dominant in this potting shed than anywhere else I had visited so far. It was in here that Lucie and Stennie had spent much of their time cuddling and caressing. Here, in the potting shed, they had almost - but not quite - had the ultimate physical relationship.

I felt strangely elated. Mr Buckley was eyeing me with curiosity and probably wondering why I had a sudden, compulsive urge to take photographs of his shed. He must have considered me a most unusual guest.

I knew with absolute certainty that it was in this shed Lucie and Stennie had discussed their plans and plotted their memorable escape. How sad it should all have come to nothing.

I decided to go for a walk. Armed as always with the tools of my trade, I set off down the drive to the main road.

At the gateway, I paused a while to see the former station house and to take a picture of Lanarth itself from the drive. What I wanted to capture was a view of the property from the angle at which Lucie last saw it: the angle at which I myself had seen it so often in my dreams. And regressions.

I walked for a mile or so along the A39 (listed on my old map as the Atlantic Highway) and as I did so, began to be overcome by feelings of familiarity again.

Though there would be no way of proving it, I KNEW that Lucie had travelled along this route with Papa. I knew it from the feel of a muff on my fingers and the impression of maroon-coloured padded leather inside the carriage doors.

I could hear the clip-clop of the horses' hooves as their evocative smell assailed my nostrils. It was a most comforting, earthy smell. It had hit me in Cobh, and it was hitting me in St Kew.

Lucie was a great one for social prestige, and travelling in style was right up her street. I can't say I object to it myself, either, and on that long walk back, the sight of a splendid horse-drawn carriage pulling up to offer me a lift would have been very welcome. Unfortunately, my manifestations are never of such a practical nature.

I was almost back at Lanarth, when I caught sight of a public house on the opposite side of the road. The Red Lion. Red Lion, I repeated to myself.

Now, why did that get the grey cells going? What was it about the Red Lion that niggled away at the back of my mind?

Yes, I was thirsty after my long walk; but no, it wasn't only thirst that was drawing me towards it. I had a stong impression of something more than that. What was it?

Surely Lucie, Lady Latymer was not in the habit of nipping out for a tipple? That did not tie in at all with what I knew of her. Had the pub served a different function back in the early days of the century, then?

What WAS it about the place that was drawing me to it so forcefully?

I crossed the road, stood for a minute at the door, then turned away. I couldn't go inside, any more than Lucie could have done. Whatever her connection with this old coaching inn, it was not inside the building.

Of that, I was sure.

NOTE, CHAPTER 19

*1 According to MacLean's History of Trigg Minor, in January 1872 the property was conveyed to the Rev. John Every, a former chaplain in the Royal Navy, and brother of the Vicar of St Kew.

Chapter 20

The Red Lion had been built in the seventeeth century and stood at the junction of three roads: the one I had just trekked along, and two at acute angles to it. A glance at my map showed that the road running behind the pub led to Trequite, the home of Mrs Routledge, whose very helpful letter had led me to Lanarth.

Earlier that day, I had tried to make contact by telephone without success. I wanted to express my gratitude by treating her to lunch, or dinner.

Only I never reached Trequite, because I got no further than the Red Lion. As I had suspected, the attraction for Lucie was not within the establishment itself. It turned out to have been BEHIND it. For there, in the corner of a patch of waste ground, was a huge stone. I sat on it, like many before and since.

What a wonderful meeting place this makeshift seat would have been for our pair. Even on the night of their escape, who would ever think of looking for them at the back of a public house?

This, said my subconscious, was where Arthur Stenning had pondered his future, those long years ago. This was where he was most likely to have acquired the horse that would transport Lucie and himself on the first leg of their journey.

In keeping with the occasion, this was where I came to sit from time to time, to ponder upon what happened next. . .

For three days, I enjoyed the comfort of that fine house and wallowed in its memories. I continued to rise at dawn and sneak into that back bedroom, to sit in the window of the room I knew instinctively to have been Lucie's: to look out again on the garden where she first set eyes on her love.

And I used up several reels of film; mostly focussing on parts of the house and grounds which struck me as being familiar. In the house itself, I took pictures of the dining room, the room that I believed was once Papa's study; the former music room, with its old iron fireplace and bay window (both of which I recognised instantly); the french window, through which Lucie was in the habit of sneaking in and out, in her stockinged feet.

I zoomed in on the staircase, with its dark oak banisters, the tall landing window and that terribly nostalgic recessed sash window in Lucie's room.

Outside, I took pictures of the house from a variety of angles: long shots, close-ups, front views, back views (unfortunately, the place was being renovated so there was a lot of scaffolding).

At the front, as I took pictures of Mr Buckley and Digger at the main entrance, I had a strong impression of elegant horsedrawn carriages clanking in and out.

Round the back, playing retrieving games with Digger, memories of similar games with Brindley flooded my mind. We crossed the rustic bridge over the stream and, finding an old tree trunk to sit on, I paused awhile to change my film. A vision of our romantic pair appeared before me. There was room enough for two, if they sat very close together.

Camera on the go once more, I snapped away; now concentrating on a stone seat, the walled garden with its old tombstone, two strangely-shaped palm trees and the one remaining stone wall of the tithe cottage.

And I closed in on lush green pathways between the trees and bushes, through which our pair would have wandered hand in hand, before hiding somewhere for their stolen kisses.

Now here was something that had not struck me before. As she chased her lover through the buses, Lucie had called her game 'skippety-hop'. Her antics were not at all ladylike, and well she knew it, but who cared when they were such tremendous fun.

I stood, transfixed, at the place where the pond would have been. It was exactly where I remembered. Looking at it then (and even studying the colour transparencies on my return) made me feel very sad.

Finding that part of the garden was the only dark moment of my stay at Lanarth. The sight of it brought back all the trauma of that moment in Lucie's little world. It made me, as it must have made her, feel as if the whole world had collapsed; that there was nothing left.

She was a child, whose mother had suddenly gone. How terrifying it must have been for her. One moment the lady was laughing happily and playing games in the garden, the next, she was gone forever. And, young though Lucie was, the child knew her mother would never play with her again.

She was alone. Water had separated her from the one person in the world that she loved above all else. At the time of the accident, Lucie would have had no idea how the accident had occured.

But, I knew that she would have been given the details just as soon as she was old enough to comprehend them. I had an impression of the Baron sitting her down in his study, presenting her with the facts about her mother's fatal accident and warning her yet again about the danger of going too near the water.

Mama had, apparently, tripped, fallen face forward into the water and hit a rock with such force that it had crushed her skull. No wonder Papa had had the pond filled in and had felt it necessary to issue continual warnings to his daughter to keep away from water (not that she had taken the slightest notice, as had been obvious from what emerged during my regressions).

On a lighter note, I also had an impression of Lucie peering through the bushes, believing that if she could not see the house from the far end of the orchard, then no-one in the house would be able to see her.

I continued to be drawn towards the potting shed: an attractive, detached building, looking for all the world like a Wendy house.

An enchanting little construction, it would have made a perfect play house for a child who enjoyed playing fantasy roles. And having played in there as a child, she continued to 'play' in it as a young woman.

I continued to amble through lawns and woods with the dog of the house, much as Lucie would have done with hers. And I ventured out to continue my wider explorations of the area. An arbitrary study of the map showed that the road from Lanarth led to Camelford in one direction, and Probus in the other.

Probus was where Mrs Lewis had told Geoff Whitfield her sister had said she was going. Even in those days, it would only have been a short drive (or ride) from Lanarth. Conclusion: Lucie and Eleanor Truelove must have been one and the same person: Lanarth must have been their home.

Having, more or less, located Lucie, could I not also find Stennie? I wrote to everyone of that name I could find in the local directory; in each case enclosing a stamped addressed envelope. Not one of them replied. It was hardly surprising. After all, it would take a brave family to admit to having had a gypsy relative who absconded with a young aristocratic lady and whisked her off to obscurity... even if it did happen 80-odd years ago.

Nevertheless, I continued to take photographs, and notes, of everything I thought even remotely connected with them: the Red Lion, the stone behind it, road signs leading to other local villages. I also photographed the large yellow sign for Lanarth itself notifying travellers that it provided bed and breakfast accommodation; had caravan and camping facilities, was a free house. . .

Chapter 21

One task remained before I set out on my long homeward journey. I had to make some attempt to determine Lucie and Stennie's mode of transport between here and the Irish port where we next found them.

On the advice of those who know about such matters, I took myself off to Port Isaac, and spent a fascinating afternoon chatting to an expert on the history of shipping in North Cornwall. My main query was how he thought our couple might have travelled to Ireland.

Well, first of all, they were not likely to have travelled on any sort of passenger ship, he told me.

"If the young man was of gypsy stock, he'd have been able to get hold of a couple of horses without too much difficulty."

Having just purchased a postcard depicting a single massed sailing vessel, I showed it to the expert and asked if the gypsy would have sold the horses and bought something like that for his lady and himself.

"Oh no. They wouldn't have taken a fishing smack to Ireland. And they certainly wouldn't have bought the boat. It would have cost too much, and anyway that sort of craft is always handed down from father to son, or uncle to nephew."

Nor would he have wanted to keep the animals, stressed the expert because gypsy horses were quite different from any others and would be too easily recognised; particularly in these parts where people used donkeys.

"He'd have got her to dress up as a boy, and they'd have had a meeting with another gypsy, to swap the horses for a bit of gold jewellery. He'd be used to doing a bit of bartering.

"She'd have to stay dressed as a boy for a while, though.

"They'd sail out on the evening tide, on a single mast fishing vessel; the sort that would have two men and a boy. The boy would act as cook, swilling the deck, catching a few fish.

"They'd travel up towards Bristol at about five miles an hour - less if the wind dropped - and the journey would take about fourteen hours.

"There wouldn't be any sleeping accommodation on that sort of craft. They'd all have to rough it on deck and their diet would be mainly salt beef, salt pork, oatmeal bread and any fish they happened to catch. It'd be mostly cod or mackerel.

"They'd berth at Bristol or Barry Island on the high tide and probably watch the pilot boats coming in and out before deciding what to do next. There'd be plenty of choice. The Bristol Channel was always a busy shipping lane.

"The most likely form of transport after that would be a cattle steamer. It'd take another forty hours to get to Cork."

There was, he added a lot of slate being shipped across to Ireland in those days, but their trip would have been somewhat precarious because of sailing against the wind and the tides.

"On the other hand, if they'd set off in a small boat from Cornwall, they could have gone right up to Holyhead; and then over to Rosslare or Cork. There were lots of coastal trading boats around at the time.

"Here in Port Isaac, the old folks say they could always recognise the boats on the Irish run, because of the black cobblestones. That was their clue that flint had come in from Ireland, as ballast.

"They traded in cloth and spirits (mainly brandy) and tobacco, to avoid paying tax. They'd come and go when the place was quiet.

"Port Isaac fishermen would never go out on a Sunday, but Padstow men would. They'd go up to Bristol with a cargo of Cornish slate, but your couple would know that. At least, he would." . .

Port Isaac was still much as it was in 1912. And now that I had visited it, I was convinced that this was indeed the port from which Lucie and Stennie had set sail.

They had NOT travelled by train. Even had the station been open when they set off that night, Lucie could not possibly have boarded a train at St. Kew. She would have been recognised, as she probably would in Wadebridge and if her father was as important as she gave us to understand, possibly even in Bodmin. Their original intention (correction, HER original intention) to travel by train, would have been quickly dismissed. The last thing on earth Lucie would have wanted would have been to be hauled back home for a severe carpetting by her father.

But I was not entirely convinced that Port Isaac was their next choice. I had a strong impression of going to Polzeath - another village not far from her home - and setting off from there.

That would account for Lucie's odd sense of familiarity when she was on board the tender heading out towards the Titanic, and gazing back at land. Queenstown - with its whitewashed cottages dotted about on the hill - bore a striking similarity to Polzeath.

At low tide, they could have ridden across to Polzeath from Rock, which was only a few miles from Lanarth. It was probably Stennie who suggested the alternative route, because he would have been more likely to know the legend of Polzeath than Lucie.

During the late 1700s, everyone in that village was lost during a dreadful storm. All the wives left the village, and fishing craft had never gone out from there since. Being of gypsy stock, Stennie would not have wanted to tempt fate by talking a fishermen into taking them out. . .

What had I gained from my brief spell at Lanarth?

Documented, conclusive proof of Lucie and Stennie's existence? Not exactly, but I did have enough evidence to convince me that they had spent their short lives hereabouts.

Gut feelings were in plentiful supply, as St Kew Highway in general and Lanarth in particular took on the same familiar feel that Cobh had done earlier that same year.

As with Cobh, I sat down and itemised the points which had emerged from past life recall in order to compare them with the reality. In this case, they slotted into four distinct groups,

CATEGORY A MEMORIES were those I had before even being consciously aware of Lanarth and certainly before ever setting foot in the place.

CATEGORY B MEMORIES were those that filtered through to my mind as soon as I had arrived.

CATEGORY C MEMORIES were the overflow from category A, but which had to be separated from them because they could not be authenticated.

CATEGORY A contained six points::

* One The house itself. It DID exist, was large, white and had a tall, landing window.
* Two It also had a cellar
* Three And extensive grounds, including streams and an orchard
* Four The garden pond had been there many years ago, but it had long since been filled in.
* Five The railway station house still stood at the gates of Lanarth, though the station itself was no longer functional; trains had ceased to run many years ago and the track had been dismantled.
* Six A family with the surname provided by Lucie DID live in the house at some stage; though, admittedly, the dates are a little haywire.

CATEGORY B went even better, with eight points.

* One The peacocks.
* Two French window, which would not normally be seen by guests (how could I possibly have known it was there, unless I was actually familiar with the house, which - in this life - I was not.)
* Three Papa's study and music room
* Four The window seat in Lucie's bedroom
* Five The potting shed
* Six Horses and carriages in the driveway
* Seven Practically every inch of the garden!
* Eight The stone in the waste ground behind the Red Lion.

CATEGORY C had just two points:

* One The existence of Brindley

* Two The pair of Doric columns that I felt had been part of the house's original frontage.

I made exhaustive enquiries to see if anyone, anywhere could produce a picture of Lanarth (or Newton House, as it was originally known), showing these columns; so far, without success. One day, perhaps, someone will be able to confirm, or deny their existence. . .

Lanarth, house of dreams.
Picture by the author.

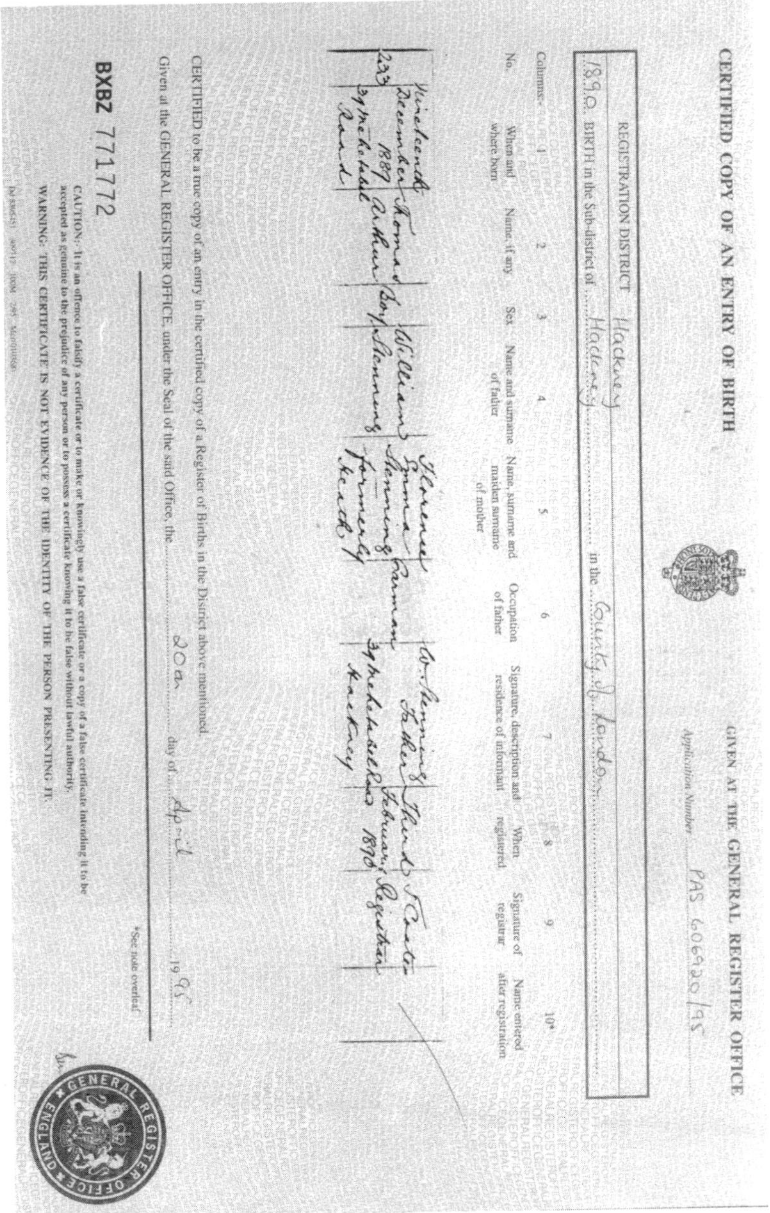

CERTIFIED COPY OF AN ENTRY OF BIRTH

GIVEN AT THE GENERAL REGISTER OFFICE

Application Number PAS 606920/95

REGISTRATION DISTRICT Hackney

1890. BIRTH in the Sub-district of Hackney in the County of London

Columns:- 1	2	3	4	5	6	7	8	9	10*
No. When and where born	Name, if any	Sex	Name and surname of father	Name, surname and maiden surname of mother	Occupation of father	Signature, description and residence of informant	When registered	Signature of registrar	Name entered after registration
233 Nineteenth December 1889 39 Mehetabel Road	Thomas Arthur	Boy	William Hemming	Florence Emma Hemming formerly Keech	Fireman	W. Hemming Father 39 Mehetabel Road Hackney	Third February 1890	J. Coates Registrar	

*See note overleaf

CERTIFIED to be a true copy of an entry in the certified copy of a Register of Births in the District above mentioned.

Given at the GENERAL REGISTER OFFICE, under the Seal of the said Office, the 20th day of April 1995

BXBZ 771772

CAUTION: It is an offence to falsify a certificate or to make or knowingly use a false certificate or a copy of a false certificate intending it to be accepted as genuine to the prejudice of any person or to possess a certificate knowing it to be false without lawful authority.

WARNING: THIS CERTIFICATE IS NOT EVIDENCE OF THE IDENTITY OF THE PERSON PRESENTING IT.

GENERAL REGISTER OFFICE ENGLAND

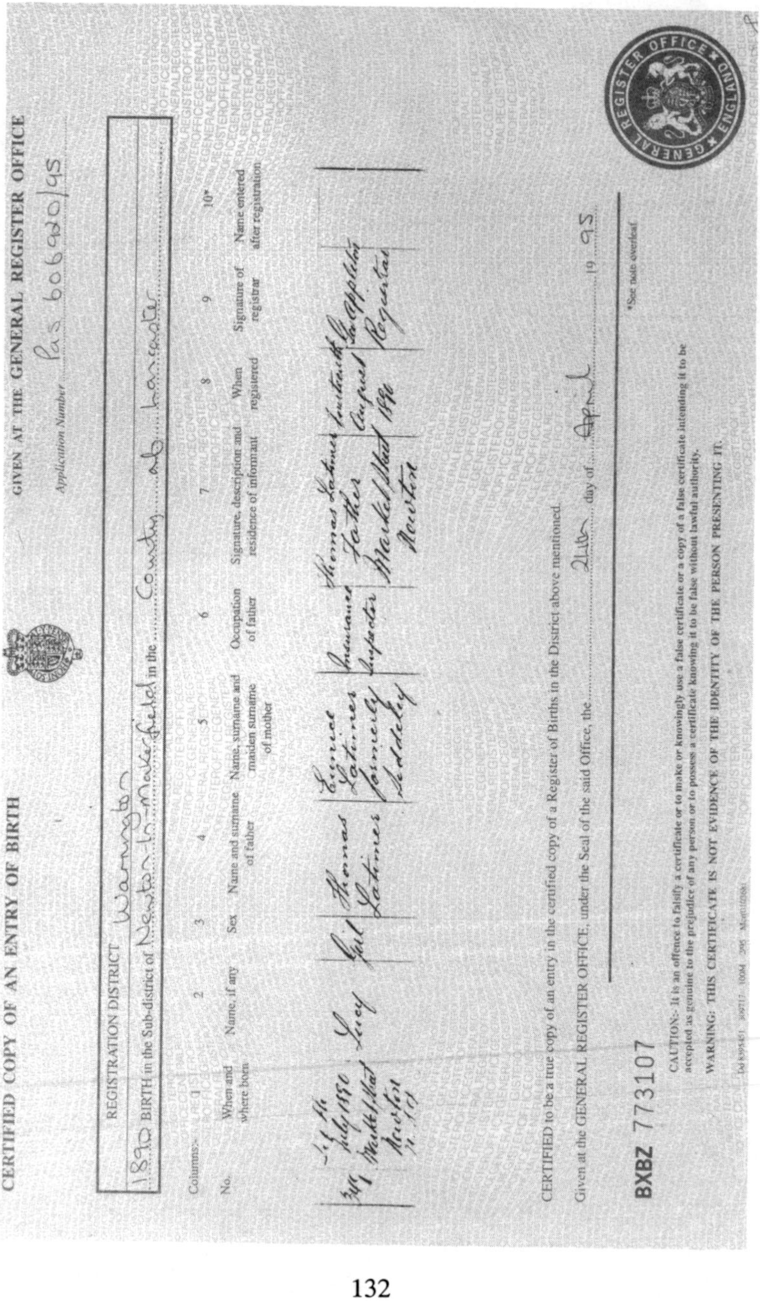

CERTIFIED COPY OF AN ENTRY OF BIRTH

GIVEN AT THE GENERAL REGISTER OFFICE

Application Number Pas 606920/95

REGISTRATION DISTRICT Warrington

1890 BIRTH in the Sub-district of Newton-In-Makerfield in the County of Lancaster

Columns:- 1	2	3	4	5	6	7	8	9	10*
No. When and where born	Name, if any	Sex	Name and surname of father	Name, surname and maiden surname of mother	Occupation of father	Signature, description and residence of informant	When registered	Signature of registrar	Name entered after registration
[illegible] July 1890 Market Street Newton [illegible]	Lucy	Girl	Thomas Latimer	Eunice Latimer formerly Seddeley	Insurance Inspector	Thomas Latimer Father Market Street Newton	Fourteenth August 1890	G. Appleton Registrar	

CERTIFIED to be a true copy of an entry in the certified copy of a Register of Births in the District above mentioned.

Given at the GENERAL REGISTER OFFICE, under the Seal of the said Office, the 24th day of April 1995

*See note overleaf

BXBZ 773107

CAUTION:- It is an offence to falsify a certificate or to make or knowingly use a false certificate or a copy of a false certificate intending it to be accepted as genuine to the prejudice of any person or to possess a certificate knowing it to be false without lawful authority.

WARNING: THIS CERTIFICATE IS NOT EVIDENCE OF THE IDENTITY OF THE PERSON PRESENTING IT.

PART FIVE

Chapters 22 - 25

Developments

Chapter 22

Queenstown had suddenly become a hive of activity.

The reason for the upsurge of interest was that the town's Heritage Trust had recently launched an exciting exhibition entitled Cobh, The Queenstown Story.

Opened on March 3, 1993, by the then Taoiseach (Prime Minister) Albert Reynolds, the exhibition attracted more than 90,000 visitors in its first season, arousing considerable interest in both Britain and America.

It also won major awards from the Irish American Cultural Institution, the Allied Irish Bank and others, locally based. During November/ December, 1993, almost 1,500 American travel agents called in to look over the centre and consider its possibilities as a tourist attraction for their clients.

They all appeared to have been highly impressed with the way Cobh's history and legacy had been restored.

The exhibition, now permanently based at the re-vamped Victorian Railway Station, depicts the story not just of Titanic's visit, but of other aspects of shipping in the area and mass emigration from the port.

Lesley Kelly, a spokesperson for Cobh's Heritage Centre, told me that visitors of all ages and from all walks of life were describing the project as a most worthwhile way of interpreting history. Between 1848 and 1950, of the six million adults and children who emigrated from Ireland; some 2.5 million left Cobh, making it the country's single most important port of emigration across the Atlantic.

Innumerable emigrants setting off via Cobh travelled on the dreaded coffin ships[*1] and never actually arrived in America. There were more passengers on those ships than on all the early steamers and the great ocean liners put together.

The latest venture for Cobh Heritage Trust, I was told, was to spearhead a campaign to honour those who spent their final hours in the land of their birth. Invitations had gone out to anyone whose ancestors might have passed through the port en route to America, to place the names of those ancestors on display.

Each individual or family name would then be displayed for posterity on a Wall of Dedication in the Heritage Centre. They would also be inscribed on a special certificate which would be given to surviving members of the family.

In addition, all names together with those of the donors, would be entered into the centre's computer register.

Cobh Heritage Trust is to be congratulated on its achievements, but I am glad I visited the town when I did... i.e., before all these facts about the town, its people and its building became public knowledge. Otherwise, I would probably not have dug so deeply into its records and thus might have been deprived of the pleasure of doing my own 'detective' work.

There's nothing quite like the joy of discovery: be it seeing the first snowdrop of spring, hearing the glorious music of Palestrina, or simply the results of straightforward journalistic research.

For the benefit of those who might also be interested in what the town and its environs have to offer, here are ten further facts about Cobh:

* The Cove of Cork was a marshalling centre for British troop ships in the American War of Independence, Boer and Crimean Wars.
* Rebels from the 1798 Uprising and Robert Emmet's 1803 Rebellion were among the 30,000 men and 9,000 women transported as convicts from Cove/Queenstown between 1791 and 1853.
* The Sirius, captained by a Corkman, Richard Roberts, became the first vessel to cross the Atlantic entirely under steam power in April, 1838.
* Between 1845 and 1851, the town was the departure point for 1.5 million Irish emigrants to the United States - more than the entire volume of emigrants in the previous 50 yearsbut then, this period incorporated the Great Potato Famine of 1845-1847, when there was a mass exodus from the country.

* Famine relief was shipped to Ireland from the United States when the 'Jamestown' brought 800 tons of food into Cork in 1847, to be followed two months later by the relief ship, 'Macedonia', also bringing food.
* More than 4,000 orphan girls from workhouses were transported as domestic servants to Australia between 1848 and 1850 (many of these children would have been orphaned during the famine).
* The coming of the railway to the town in 1862 gave the port an enhanced role in the mail services between North America and the United Kingdom. Mail was both received and despatched from the port, which was within easy reach of all major centres in the British Isles. It was appropriate that the line to Cobh had a world class engineer, namely Isambard Kingdom Brunel.*[2]
* On January 1, 1892, Annie Moore from County Cork became the first emigrant processed through Ellis Island, New York, when landing from a vessel which had sailed from Queenstown.

  It was her 15th birthday.
* Between 1848 and 1900, Irish emigrants in America sent home more than £46 million to families in Ireland.
* The exhibition: Cobh, The Queenstown Story is situated in the former American consulate building (overlooking the former railway station), where aspiring emigrants were tested for their proficiency in English. Today, the building is an Irish language school. . .

In the middle of my research into Irish aspects of the Titanic, I received some poignant Titanic reminders from a parish priest in Co. Mayo, in the West of the country.

Canon Seamus Boland, of Ballina, sent me copies of seven baptismal certificates, extracted from the ledgers of the diocese of Killala. They were those of John Bourke, Pat Canavan, Bridget Donohoe, James Flynn, Bridget McDermott, Bridget (Delia) Mahon and Mary Mangan: seven babies, born in the 1880s and 1890s, in the lakeside village of Lahardane.

The infants grew up, reached maturity and I am indebted to fellow researchers Tom Williams and Geoff Whitfield for giving me the story of what happened to them.

Finding no employment in their native land, the seven teamed with other young men and women of the village and bought themselves tickets to America in the belief that a future in the New World would be brighter than that which might face them at home. (These would have been Lucy and her escort's fellow steerage passengers: the travellers whom she regarded with such disdain. Perhaps they thought even less of her!).

John Bourke was taking his wife, Catherine and his sister Mary. Pat Canavan was escorting his cousin, also named Mary. James Flynn, an American resident for some time, was returning to his brother's home after a visit to their parents. Their party totalled 13: an unlucky number, as it turned out. Eleven of them never returned.

When news of the tragedy reached Lahardane, the entire village was plunged into sadness. Wakes, held by their grieving families, ran for two days and two nights, during which time mourners from all over the country converged on the tiny cottages to offer their condolences.

A pall hung over the village as its people laid out their dead. Only their dead were two thousand miles away. It was the clothes of the absent victims that lay on the covers. Photographs of each victim were placed where the faces should be. Then the beds (including that so recently occupied by John and Catherine Bourke) were covered with snow-white quilts and surrounded by lighted candles.

NOTES, CHAPTER 22

*1 The term 'coffin ships' applied to un-seaworthy vessels sent to sea before the introduction of the Plimsoll line; which indicated the maximum depth to which ships may be loaded.

*2 Isambard Kingdom Brunel (1806-1859) planned Clifton suspension bridge in 1829; then, as a naval architect, designed the Great Britan (the first oceangoing screw steamer) and the Great Eastern, (another famous ocean-going steamer.)

Chapter 23

Discovery of Lanarth had represented a major breakthrough in my search for Lucie/Lucy. My spine still tingled at the memories that house and its surroundings revived. I had high hopes of cracking the story once and for all. My disappointment was all the greater, then, when the trail went cold.

Circumstances, however, were not exactly conducive to writing, at the time. Deeply upset over the death of our beloved Great Dane, following the deaths of two elderly German Shepherds - all in a matter of 14 months - I was in no mood for tracking down Lucy.

So, without meaning to renew her agonies, I put my Lady of Lanarth on ice. . .

It was a full year before I resumed the idea of writing her story and, even then, I wasn't sure in which direction I (or she) was going.

In January 1994, the magazine Reincarnation International, was born and it sparked off new hope. Jack Pleasant, a journalist friend living in Sussex, wrote a feature on my regression and media interest was aroused again, with various Press, radio and television journalists picking up the story.

Jack specialises in various esoteric subjects and has written extensively about reincarnation, telepathy, cryptomnesia, and so on.

Having featured many of Joe Keeton regressions, the story of Lucie Latymer and her association with the Titanic completely captivated him.

He recounted her escapades to readers in Britain,*[1] America,*[2] and the United Arab Emirates.*[3]

Roy Stemman, the magazine's editor sent us a copy of the first issue, featuring some fascinating cases and, predictably, issue number two contained a feature on the elusive Lucie Latymer*[4] . . .

Towards the end of 1994, I decided to visit The Wreck of the Titanic Exhibition, then running at the Maritime Museum in Greenwich, London. The exhibition had already been open for a month or more, but I had been postponing the visit because of conflicting emotions. At that stage, I was not entirely sure I approved of the idea of Titanic memorabilia being brought up from the depths of the ocean, to be exposed to all and sundry.

Those who had already visited the exhibition gave me to understand that it was well worth seeing, as it featured the first major display of artefacts recovered from the seabed. Apparently, it gave a fascinating insight into the lives and expectations of those who sailed away on that tragic maiden voyage.

I still had reservations.

What right had anyone, however well intentioned, to remove those items; to 'plunder a grave'?

It could, I supposed, be argued that what the sea had stolen, the sea should return and I had to admit that the circumstances surrounding the tragedy did captivate me.

They had already drawn me to exhibitions in the maritime museums of Liverpool and Belfast.

Curiosity, which had started me off on the road to regression four years earlier, was surfacing again... now to push me along the road to London.

But even as I made my way to Greenwich, I argued that neither the Liverpool nor the Belfast exhibition had involved anyone actually going down and bringing items up from the actual ship. I had yet to discover that this latest one did not either. The objects featured had all come from the area SURROUNDING the wreck.

The facts:

* The wreck was discovered on September 1, 1985, by a Franco-American scientific expedition. The expedition was led by Dr. Robert Ballard of the Woods Hole Oceanographic Institution and Captain Jean-Louis Michel of the Institut Francais de Recherche pour l' exploration des Meres (IFREMER).

  Captain Michel was in command of the watch aboard the R/V Knorr when Titanic's wreck was first spotted on the underseas cameras.

  Ballard, who was off duty, was roused from his cabin; he came to the instrument room and immediately took over.

  The findings of these two men confirmed what most people had already suspected: the ship had split in two (bow and stern now lying about 600 metres apart).

* Ten months later, Dr Ballard returned to the wreck with a second expedition. Landing the submersible Alvin on her decks, he explored and photographed the entire wreck and debris field in detail. What few people realised until the story of the discovery broke was that debris was spread over an area the size of the City of London.

* The first United States legislation was introduced in the United States House of Representatives on September 11, 1985, less than two weeks after the wreck's discovery. It was introduced by Representative Walter B. Jones, Chairman, Committee on Merchant, Marine and Fisheries, United States House of Representatives, and was designated HR 3273, 99th Congress, First Session. Its title: 'The RMS Titanic Maritime Memorial Act of 1985'.

  Hearings were held during October 1985, and the Bill was passed by the House of Representatives on December 3, 1985.

  It was then sent to the United States Senate where, after revisions, it was passed on October 6, 1986 and signed into law by the (then) President Ronald Reagan on October 21, 1986.

* The first artefacts were recovered in 1987 by Titanic Ventures (later RMS Titanic, Inc.), who are the legal owners of the wreck. The company was declared 'salver in possession' by the Federal District Court for the Eastern District of Virginia, USA.[*6]

* A year after this second Ballard expedition, the U.S. Congress moved to make the Titanic an international memorial. .

"We did a great deal of research and thinking before deciding it was right to go ahead with the idea," confessed Laura Weston, the museum's public relations manager.

The exhibition proved to be sensitively handled and totally unsensational.

"We've tried to be objective, by representing all points of view. These artefacts provide a point of contact both for people who've lost relatives on the ship and for those who simply want to learn more about the event," I was told.

"We feel the social and historical aspects surrounding the ship and her tragic loss are very important for future generations. The idea is to educate and commemmorate: what has been brought up is now preserved for posterity."

The purpose of the exhibition was basically to chronicle the events and circumstances surrounding the tragedy, and to focus attention on the whole business of bringing up memorabilia.

Richard Ormond, the museum's director, "The tragedy of the Titanic - still one of the world's worst maritime disasters - has entered the realm of legend. But the objects in the exhibition remind us of the reality. They bear witness to the ship, her story and the world of 1912, from which they came... and through them, the memory of those who died may live on.". .

What effect did browsing through this treasure trove of social history have on me? Did I recognise any objects, experience any strange feelings?

I did, and it was a thoroughly enlightening experience; positively eerie at times. All five senses were aroused... sound, touch, taste, smell and sight; in that order.

SOUND: It was the positively eerie hoot of the funnels that first struck me. Blasting away in the opening section, they were supposed to set the scene for the start of the voyage. In my mind, they were more reminiscent of the end and gave me a feeling of very great discomfort. I felt an urgent need to escape.

Did the funnels hoot as the ship was about to sink? Or was Lucie one of the many unfortunate passengers crushed when a giant funnel toppled forward in what has been described as a cloud of soot and sparks, flattening the starboard bridge wing? For me, the latter explanation is the most likely, because I KNOW that Lucie spent most of her time at the stern, where she was supposed to sleep... but seldom did.

First hand memories coming through in relation to the next three senses were also pretty potent.

TOUCH: A bench end, ornate and scrolled, was one of several found scattered in debris field. One glance at that bench end and I was there again, feeling the chill of the North Atlantic weather and the damp of the ocean spray.

TASTE: That came from sight of a mug, brought up from the area near the third class section. I knew instinctively Lucie had been served beef tea in one of those. Yet a feeling of revulsion swept over me, which had nothing to do with beef tea, but was directly related to the mug itself. Lucie would never have drunk from THAT. Why?

Because it was cracked and chipped. (I, Monica, know that was a ridiculous reaction... the mug would not have been chipped at the time).

Was this a case of Lucie looking at the mug through my eyes, or was I looking at it through hers? I could almost taste the beef tea. On a broader level, this sort of item was a salutary reminder of the slice of life in the early days of this century Titanic and her people represented.

The mugs in steerage contrasted sharply with the fine bone china cups provided for first and second class passengers.

SMELL: Examining the dinner forks made me long to touch them, to get the feel of them in my hand, but that was not possible. Like everything else, these items were protected in a glass case. And rightly so. But a sudden smell of beef and pickled onions pervaded my nostrils, as if Lucie were about to tuck into that final high tea on board.

(Third class passengers were, in fact served ragout of beef and pickled onions on Sunday. The meal turned out to be their last, which was probably why that particular smell was most dominant in Lucie's memory).

SIGHT: That was the strongest experience of all. Sight of the model and plot of the stern section and debris field saddened me for two reasons: first, because the life of that lovely ship should have ended in this way and secondly because, as already pointed out, I'm convinced that Lucie's final hours were spent at the stern. Seeing those 'before and after' models was particularly upsetting.

Sauntering along to a recessed area of the exhibition, I stopped dead in my tracks. For I had come face to face with a lifesized portrayal of the grand staircase and its surrounding area.

The section was so arranged that, from where they stood, visitors could feel as if they were actually on board. Suddenly, it was as if I were peering into a looking glass, because the artist's impression included the figure of a slim young girl in a blue dress, sweeping elegantly down the staircase; long, white fingers holding on to the banister.

This was uncanny.

I could not have depicted Lucie better myself. It was the very situation I had referred to in chapter seven (just before she reached the bottom of the stairs and was challenged about the status of her ticket). Those notes were penned at least six weeks before my visit.

I was utterly entranced. . .

The exhibition proved illuminating and I couldn't help wondering what would happen to all the artefacts when it ended.

There would be no question of anything being sold to any private collector, stressed the organisers. The long-term intent of RMS Titanic Inc.'s research and recovery programme was to keep the artefacts recovered from the ship together as a collection and make them available for exhibition to the public.

In November, 1994, the Law of the Sea Convention was ratified by 67 countries.

The exhibition, originally intended to run only until October 1994, was extended to April, 1995. By the time it closed, it had been viewed by almost 750,000 visitors and was the most popular in the history of the National Maritime Museum.

In February 1995, the Museum held an international conference to promote the development of new legislation to protect historic shipwreck sites in international waters.

NOTES, CHAPTER 23

*1 Pleasant, Jack and Cathy Burden: Heal the Past, Woman's Realm, August 4, 1992, p.29

*2 Pleasant, Jack: When I Died on the Titanic, Gulf News, Dubai, October 12, 1993, p.12

*3 Pleasant, Jack: I Died on the Titanic in my Past Life, Globe, USA, November, 1993

*4 Pleasant, Jack, Reincarnation International, April, 1994, No.2, p.5

*5 The Wreck of the Titanic Exhibition, National Maritime Museum, Greenwich, London, October 4, 1994 - April 2, 1995

*6 Information received in author's correspondence with John P. Eaton.

Chapter 24

January, 1995

My New Year resolution was to find documented evidence of the existence of Lucie/ and/or Stennie, to corroborate all the information I already had about both. The obvious place to start was with the General Register Office Indexes of St Catherine's House (formerly Somerset House), London: which lists every birth, marriage and death registered in England and Wales.

Setting out to work my way through the many minuscule entries made in the latter days of the 19th century, I was thankful that my characters were not named Smith, or Jones. The search began in 1900 and from there I flicked backwards; ploughing through thirty-four microfilmed versions of the General Index of Births, stored at Liverpool Central Library. The reels contained entries of every recorded birth in the UK: thousands upon thousands of them.

Between the Lathams and the La Touches, I found a variety of Latimers (mostly male), Lattemores and, further down the screen, a few Lattimers, but not a single entry for Latymer. The name Stenning only cropped up occasionally and the entries bore no resemblance whatever to the character for whom I searched.

After a five-hour non-stop stint, my finger hit on the year 1890. I had struck gold.

Not only had I found what could have been the elusive young lady,[*1] but I had also located her beau (of whom, more anon).[*2]

Ah... but if this was my alter-ego, she was not Lucie, as the snooty voice of my subconscious had kept insisting.

Nor was she Latymer 'with a y'. She was just plain, ordinary Lucy Latimer. To confound the issue further, she had been born many miles from Cornwall: in Warrington, actually... then Lancashire, now Cheshire.

To have been born in the middle of 1890 would have made her twenty-one years old at the time of the Titanic disaster. And it had already been established that the runaways were in their early twenties, despite the fact that I had always imagined the girl to be younger.

If this was the character for whom I searched, what was going on? Why did she appear 'Up North', instead of where I had expected her to? Had the house moves, referred to so vaguely in regression, covered all these miles?

Had death or divorce separated Lucy's parents, and what had become of each partner?

Remembering only too well that all that 'glistened'*[3] need not necessarily be gold was it, I wondered, the fools' variety I had struck? As ever, in our infuriating game of hide and seek, I found myself yet again running round in circles: Cornwall, Cork, and now Lancashire. Where WAS the girl, for heaven's sake?

'I'm here... there... just around the corner. Find me.... Find me....' . .

If this was the 'real' Lucy, had her mother taken up with Sandys at Lanarth, to become A.N. Other, as mentioned in the deeds of the house (chapter 17)?

Was Sandys the autocratic gentleman known as Papa?

All right, so the deeds were dated 1885, but if the Sandys gentleman had been in the habit of keeping anonymous lady friends under his roof, the A.N.Other could have covered a multitude of mistresses. Couldn't it...?

Lucie (I still thought of her with that spelling) referred to Mama's having drowned in the pond, and again the house deeds did show that there was a pond in the grounds, though it had been filled in long before living memory. Milady was definitely at Lanarth at some stage of her life. Otherwise, how would I (in this life) have recognised its every nook and cranny?

How else could I have been so well informed about what went on within the walls of that house (not to mention the garden and the potting shed)? As has already been indicated, that one return trip was enough to bring back intimate involvement all over again. . .

The boyfriend, who appears on the registers as Thomas Arthur Stenning, first saw the light of day some six months earlier than Lucy. In his case, the event took place in London. Birth registers only provide the name, place and quarter of the year in which the birth occured. Sight of the actual certificates is necessary for those seeking further information.

My next approach, therefore, was to the Office of Population, Censuses and Surveys (OPCS). Armed with the necessary references, I asked for copies of the two birth certificates. Arthur's place of birth was not important. He hailed from a family of travellers, so would have moved around before arriving in Cornwall.

Although I now knew him to have been born in Hackney - a deprived inner city area in East London - I still had the distinct impression of a Celtic connection somewhere along the line.*4. .

Arthur's birth certificate, which arrived within the week, gave his date of birth as December 19, 1889 and described the occupation of his father, William, as 'carman'... a traveller, just as I had constantly maintained.

Four days later, Lucy's birth certificate also landed on my doormat. Shock... horror! Her father was not a baron at all. He was an insurance inspector, named Thomas. Mama's name was Eunice and my alter-ego (?) was born on July 6, 1890 in Market Street, Newton-in-Makerfield, a town now known as Newton-le-Willows. A pretty little place, it is half way between Liverpool and Manchester in one direction, Warrington and Wigan in the other.

Contemporary street directories (Kelly's) point out: 'Lord Newton, JP, is Lord of the Manor of the barony of Newton'. Newton? Lord Newton? The barony...? It will be recalled that Lanarth was formerly known as Newton House. Co-incidence, of course!

Although there was no indication that Thomas Latimer had any aristocratic connections, he was certainly several rungs higher up the social ladder than the carman, William Stenning. Stenning might have been going nowhere, except around country lanes in his gypsy caravan, but Thomas Latimer was rising ever higher.

He must have become quite prosperous because, by the time the 1905 street directories were published, he was listed as living at Cross Lane, Earlestown (also in Lancashire), his neighbours being a doctor, solicitor, accountant, architect, publisher, music teacher and an estate agent. The grand-sounding Royal Hotel was also in Cross Lane. . .

Earlestown? Earl... earls..? Distant bells began to ring in my mind. Hadn't the child Lucy referred to an earl, or earls? Only now, did I make the connection and wonder if this was what she was trying to tell us. . .

The fact that I could find no subsequent reference to Thomas Latimer would suggest two possibilities. Either he moved out of the area: onwards and upwards. Or he died; leaving his widow and small daughter to make a new life for themselves, elsewhere.

And here, I must express my gratitude to Rita Warmington, of the Cornwall Family History Society, for her painstaking research on my behalf. Flicking through the 1881 Census for Cornwall, she unearthed particulars of an Elizabeth Latimer living at St Kew Highway with her son and daughter.[*5]

The year in question was too early for Lucy and her mother, but not for Elizabeth to have been Lucy's paternal grandmother, or grand-aunt. Even if Lucy never actually lived in St Kew, she may well have spent long holidays at Lanarth and regarded the house as her second home. After just one visit, I became very attached to it myself. It was that sort of house.

"The family was not born in Cornwall and indeed Latimer is a name which features very rarely in Cornwall," explained Mrs Warmington; confirming the comments of Angela Broome, (chapter 17) and adding credibility to the family's Lancashire connections. . .

At this point, forgive me if I digress and make a confession which might seem neither relevant nor appropriate to the matter in hand, but it is both.

I make it simply to indicate the sort of obnoxious child I was (and, though it pains me to admit it, how - in that one respect - very like Lucie/Lucy).

My maiden name was Harding: Monica Harding... but I occasionally sought to make it look more interesting on paper; spelling it, during one particular period of adolescent affectation, as Monika Hardinge; Christian and surname both taking on a brand new look.

Like Liza, with a zee*6 I became Hardinge with an e; the appealing appendage having originated in a history lesson during which I learned of the existence of Sir Henry Hardinge (1785 - 1856), first Viscount of Lahore and governor general of India (1840-47). His name, apparently, was mis-spelt as Harding (without the e) in Army lists of the period.*7

In 1809, he was promoted to major on particular service in Portugal, and I KNOW that there is a Major Harding(e) back several generations in my own family tree.

With all that in mind, I reasoned that our branch of the family had also spelt the name incorrectly and I 'adopted' Sir Henry.

I did not, however, cling to that identity as Lucy appears to have done. Nor did I go to the extent of claiming the nobleman as a father. I am not THAT old and, anyway, I was perfectly happy with the father I already had, thank you very much.

In the light of this little snippet, one must ask oneself, was I influencing Lucy to change the spelling of her name and claim aristocratic ancestry, or was Lucy influencing me to do likewise?

Whichever conclusion can be drawn, it still does not answer the question about how I (Monica) could have known so much about the barony of Latymer; including the fact of its going into abeyance. I can state, hand on heart, that I have never, in this life, met anyone by the name of Latimer, Latymer, Lattimer, Lattemore, or any other version of the name.

But some part of me is VERY familiar with it.

NOTES, CHAPTER 24

*1 Birth registers for July/Aug./Sep. 1890 show Latimer, Lucy; b.Warrington; Vol.8c,P.178

*2 Ibid. Jan./Feb./Mar 1890, Stenning, Thomas Arthur; b.Hackney, Vol.lb,P.522

*3 Gray,Thos: Ode on the Death of a Favourite Cat: Nor all that glisters, gold.

*4 It was to be a further 12 months before the 'Celtic connection' became apparent and it turned out not to have been anything to do with the Stennings.

*5 1881 Census for England and Wales, RG11/filmpiece 2293/ folio 6

*6 Leigh, Wendy: Liza Minnelli, Born a Star, New English Library, Hodder and Stoughton (1993), pp 111/2. The song, Liza, with a Z. was written by Fred Ebb, taped at the New York Lyceum and given its first public airing in 1972

*7 The Concise Dictionary of National Biography, Oxford University Press (1965), p.570 (xxiv.342).

Chapter 25

Five months had now passed since Lucy Latimer and Arthur Stenning's birth certificates came into my possession, and I was still searching relentlessly for those vital missing clues: pursuing various lines of enquiry in the quest for information about the couple and their lifestyle. Tying up those loose ends had become a priority.

At this point anything, absolutely anything, in the way of further documentation that might link the two on the birth certificates with the two on Titanic would be welcome. . .

My first course was to have another search through the St. Catherine's House registers: this time in case any marriages (even deaths) were recorded. Nothing came to light.

At the Probate Registry, I hunted through the heavy tomes to see what I could find; again, the search proved fruitless. I did not actually expect to discover anything exciting, but in the interest of accuracy, felt no stone should be left unturned.

Had the registers contained the names of either or both of our characters, then obviously they were not those for whom I was searching. In any event, I hardly think that Lucy would have been sensible enough to have made a Will.

Arthur Stenning, in view of his erstwhile nomadic lifestyle and general lack of funds, would be even less likely to have done so.

A Latimer family is known to have lived in St Kew around the period in question, but I was assured by Liz Bartlett at The Rectory in St Endellion that there were no burials in St Kew churchyard up to 1912.[*1]

If Lucy and Stennie actually did travel to Ireland together, could they have been secretly married in Cork? Catholic and Protestant avenues were both explored in an attempt to find a marriage certificate. Nothing at all was recorded under any of the three names: Lennon, Latimer, or Stenning.

A search was then made through Lancashire and Cheshire records for any information about the families of the missing pair. Trying to obtain information dating back to what I hate to admit was a very ordinary family living in very ordinary circumstances almost a century ago is never easy.

The only hope was that I might stumble across some elderly individual with a long, long memory, who might just be able to locate a needle in my haystack. . .

Still with the eloping couple in mind, I had been making various broadcasts. I put out a request through BBC Radio Merseyside, which covers the relevant areas of Lancashire and Cheshire. When weather conditions are favourable, this station also beams out to North Wales, up to the Scottish Borders, across to the Isle of Man and parts of Ireland.

I told its half-a-million listeners that what I was seeking any information relating to a Latimer family living in Newton-leWillows during the turn of the century.

Feeling that it was possible there might be some living descendants or distant relatives, I made it clear that the enquiry had nothing to do with any criminal investigation, but was purely for research purposes in connection with a book I was writing. There was no no response. People's memories are long, but obviously not that long.

Then I tried one of the RTE stations in Dublin; through a live chat show going out nationally and at a peak listening time. The station is picked up at many points in England, Scotland and Wales. This time, it was the Lennons I was after, but again, without much success: except for one quirky little follow-up call.

The RTE researcher subsequently telephoned me to say that a listener had telephoned from the Irish midlands to say that he knew of an elderly brother and sister named Denis and Mary Lennon living quite near him. He did not specify where and did not wish to approach them unless I thought it might produce the information I wanted. He gave no details other than to say they were very, very old. Did I want him to have a word with them?

Hardly, said I, since they were still alive. Asking the researcher to thank the caller on my behalf, I dismissed him and his elderly pair from my mind, put the name similarity down to coincidence and assured the researcher it was not worth pursuing.

Later on, I began to wonder if I should have been so hasty; but the second thoughts came too late. I had no phone number for the contact and no address for his elderly neighbours.

Just how old was 'very old', I kept asking myself? If there actually was some sort of connection, I was unable to work out what it might be.

During the next couple of months more pleas went out via similarly-themed features in the journals of The Irish Titanic Historical Society,[*2] and the British Titanic Society.[*3]

In the first, I asked for general information about the Lennons. The second, which related to the Latimer/Stenning connection was more specific. Having provided details of the date and place of each birth, I explained: 'What has yet to be determined is how, when and why Lucy's family travelled to Cornwall, where they were subsequently found to be.' It was a long shot, but in this type of research even the tiniest snippet can be important.

Correspondence with police headquarters at Exeter, asking if whoever was in charge would mind rummaging through old records to - determine whether Lucy Latimer or Arthur Stenning were reported missing around the time of Titanic's sailing, produced negative results. As I half expected, few records had survived from the period. The Curator of Devon and Cornwall Constabulary's Force Museum was unable to turn up anything of significance. There was no point in contacting Lancashire or Merseyside police. The family was well gone by 1912, as already explained.

The next pertinent question must be how the couple managed to pass themselves off as the Lennon siblings: or 'Lemon' as the passenger lists would have them. (Presumably with suitably acquired brogues.)

That is a difficult one to answer; because, obviously, they would have needed passports and sundry documents for US immigration purposes.

Initially, I wondered if they had stolen these items from a genuine Mary and Denis Lennon; unwittingly repeating the action of an anonymous thief in Southampton. Shortly before Titanic began her momentous journey, the thief had slipped into a local pub, found crewman

T. Hart too drunk to sail and helped himself to the crewman's discharge book. Then, no doubt feeling rather pleased with himself, he had trotted off, joined the stragglers at the end of the queue waiting to sign on and, in the name of Thomas Hart, joined his fellow crew members on deck.

The man's true identity was never discovered because he was lost in the tragedy. But for the fact that the real Thomas Hart eventually turned up at his mother's home (and gave her the shock of her life - the authorities having already informed her that he was dead) the theft may never have come to light.*4

Could our pair have been guilty of a similar crime?

Or was there a totally different explanation?

Should I not have been so rash in dismissing the idea of the very old Denis and Mary Lennon living in the Irish midlands? Just how old is 'very old'? Late nineties? A hundred plus?

The surviving pair would be at about the right age for 'my' brother and sister. I could have kicked myself for not pursuing that angle when the RTE researcher approached me... not, I feel, that it would have been entirely fair to expect the elderly siblings to dredge up memories from their distant past.

On the other hand, they might have been delighted to talk. Now, we shall never know. It is yet another gadfly I have been unable to capture.

If our eloping couple did not steal their tickets, perhaps they paid someone to produce false documents. It might not have cost too much and Lucy would probably have had enough cash at her disposal, even if Stennie had not.

One must remember too that in 1912, Queenstown was a very busy port for trans-Atlantic shipping and the day Titanic came to call was particularly chaotic. It was the Thursday of Easter week and many visitors had flocked there for the first of the year's holidays. On top of that, Queenstown was the centre of activities for the Cork Spring Show, taking place that week. The yachting fraternity was in town.

Thousands of people were milling about the place. In the circumstances, slipping through the net might not have been as difficult as it might have been a week earlier, or later. Besides, regulations were less tight in 1912 than they are today and some people managed to buy tickets right up to the last minute.

Titanic did not have her full complement of passengers. There were plenty of steerage places left and plenty of agents willing to fill them.

NOTES, CHAPTER 25

*1 Author's correspondence

*2 White Star Journal (ITHS publication), Vol.3,No.2 (1995), p.18.

*3 Atlantic Daily Bulletin (BTS journal), No.3 (1995), p.15.

*4 Eaton, John P and Charles A Haas;: Destination Disaster, PSL (1987), pp 72/3.

PART SIX

Chapters 26 - 30

Conclusions

Chapter 26

The ages of Denis and Mary Lennon, given by Jack Eaton (chapter 16) concur exactly with the birth certificates of Arthur Stenning and Lucy Latimer. The idea of a last minute acquisition of the joint ticket makes me wonder whether they had, in fact, snatched it from someone else.

Or, not to be judgmental, let us say that maybe it was all above board and they simply purchased it from two other young people who suddenly decided they did not want to go to America after all. There certainly are recorded cases of would-be passengers backing off at the eleventh hour, mainly because of premonitions and general feelings of foreboding.

An approach to James Scott and Co. (Cobh) Ltd. ship agents and brokers, was called for. Most of Titanic's Irish passengers would have had to pass through Scott's shipping office. Surely they could clarify the position?

But no. Mr Taft[*1] told me: "The company has moved offices on about four occasions since the tragedy and all files, records etc. were destroyed over the years. Unfortunately, we don't hold any records of the Titanic."

How easy would it have been for someone to travel under an assumed name? Much easier than we might imagine, it seems, and our eloping couple would have been in good company.[*2]

In first class, Sir Cosmo and Lady Lucile Duff-Gordon, Madame de Viliers, Erik Lindeberg-Lind, George Rosenchien, Edith Rosenbaum and Marguerite Hedwig Stehli are all known to have adopted pseudonyms.

Alfred Nourney clambered aboard with a second class ticket but immediately decided to pay the difference and change it for a first class one. It wasn't all he changed, as we shall see.

In second class; we had Michel Navratil, carrying a little boy on each arm and a name change on his ticket. Kate Florence Phillips and Elizabeth Ann Wilkinson were passing themselves off as wives of the gentlemen whose cabins they shared.

In third class, the case of Richard May and August Anderson are the only two which have so far come to light.

But back to those First Class couples...

Sir Cosmo and Lady Lucile Duff-Gordon booked themselves in as Mr and Mrs Morgan. The reason why has never been fully established. Perhaps they enjoyed travelling incognito; or perhaps it was to protect Lady Lucile, an internationallyacknowledged fashion designer. With salons in London and Paris and the intention of spreading her empire to New York, she may have felt that anonymity during the journey would give her a break.

Madame de Villiers, a minor member of the Belgian Royal Family, was calling herself Berthe Mayne, in order to escape recognition as she sailed away with her partner Quigg Baxter, whose child she was expecting. Belgian newspaper reports referred to her as 'a young lady much given to the pleasures of life.'

Erik Lindeberg-Lind became Eric Lingrey to avoid detection by his ex-wife whom he knew to be pursuing him for maintenance. When large liners were due in New York, it was customary for passengers' names to be published in the papers. Lind - Lingrey - did not give his wife credit for much intelligence.

George Rosenchien adopted the surname of his mistress Maybelle Thorne, with whom he was enjoying a world tour. Edith Rosenbaum's reason for the change was more understandable. She adopted the name of Russell, for business purposes. Marguerite Hedwig Stehli was booked under the name Frolicher, her mother's maiden name. The reason why has not been established.

Alfred Nourney upgraded himself to Baron van Drachstedt. A ladies' man, he liked to create an impression... of Count Dracula, would that be?

Meanwhile, in Second Class, the reason why Michel Navratil called himself Mr Hoffman was to protect, as he thought, the two tiny sons he had snatched from his estranged wife.

It was an action which was to give the authorities quite a headache when the father was subsequently lost and the children were saved. 'Titanic orphans' Michel Junior, aged four, and Edmond, who was two, spoke no English, which made identification extremely difficult.

To simplify matters for their partners, Kate Florence Phillips was travelling in the name of Mrs Henry Samuel Morley. Elizabeth Ann Wilkinson as Mrs Harry Faunthorpe.

Richard May's reason for becoming John Adams was because he wanted to avoid detection by the authorities, having had a paternity suit served on him.

August Anderson, a Swedish journalist renowned for his radical views, had left home in a hurry after writing a scathing article about the King. When he stepped aboard Titanic, his surname was Wennerstrom.

The Swede's character has been described by some as 'shady', but he behaved admirably on the night of the tragedy, staying on board ship almost until the end, in order to help many distraught passengers. Even when, drained of strength, he did manage to clamber aboard collapsible lifeboat A, he was still helping those weaker than himself[*3] . .

If all those other passengers could get away with assumed identities, why not Lucy and her male companion? Two contemporary newspaper reports featured the sad loss of a young couple. The Daily Mirror[*4] describes them as an Irish brother and sister.

The Cork Examiner[*5] was more explicit:'A young pair who were attached to each other from early youth, and who came to Queenstown by appointment and secured tickets in the name of brother and sister, intending to marry in America are both apparently gone.'. . .

All this, of course, leads us to the question of why the frenzied chasing about? Why the painstaking business of research through obscure channels when the answer was hitting us bang between the eyeballs, so to speak. Would the obvious solution not be to have another regression, when updated questions could be asked and the relevant responses given?

If only it were so simple.

The trouble was that, having been researching the regression for more than five years, I had so much knowledge about this matter that there was a very real danger of some of the information filtering through from by conscious mind into my subconscious.

That apart, the character of my alter-ego was such that she had never been very forthcoming with her responses. Such an awkward, non-communicative individual would have been highly unlikely to come up with any cogent answers.

Even if she knew them.

Trying to pin her down with specifics would simply not be possible. In any case, I strongly suspected that dear Lucy (or Lucie as she preferred to think of herself) was not terribly bright and this business of being too highborn to converse with 'ordinary people' was a facade to cover her distinct lack of grey matter.

NOTES, CHAPTER 26

*1 Author's correspondence

*2 Passenger information provided by Geoff Whitfield.

*3 Swedish research conducted by my daughter, Esther O'Hara-Lindblom

*4 Daily Mirror, April 18, 1912, p.4.

*5 Cork Examiner, April 20, 1912, p.8.

Chapter 27

My plea for information, published in the September (1995) issue of the Atlantic Daily Bulletin brought a response from America, where a reader claimed to have knowledge of the Lennon family. He had it on authority that Denis had been employed as an apprentice storekeeper in Athlone, Co Westmeath.

No details were available about Mary, other than that, on hearing of their son's liaison, Mr and Mrs Lennon were understood to have banned him forever from their home. Hence the young couple's decision to elope. The Lennons, like the Latimers, were forbidden to mention the 'miscreant's' name ever again; nevertheless, the story was passed down through the generations.

If this sequence of events actually did occur, then (as I saw it at the time) it added fuel to the possibility that Denis and Mary, having originally intended to carry on to America, changed their minds at the last minute. The idea of their meeting with Lucy and Arthur at Queenstown did not now seem so far-fetched. An English couple, unsure about how to obtain the necessary documentation, might well have discussed the matter with a friendly Irish couple (possibly while all four were staying at Grace O'Brien's Emigrants' Home) and done some sort of deal. The circumstances of our two were similar to those of the Lennons; their ages tallied. Recognising the relative ease with which one pair of elopees could pass themselves off as the other, was it so outlandish to suppose that, when the tenders were ready for boarding (or possibly much earlier), the couples went their separate ways?

My initial feeling was that, while the two posing as the Lennons boarded the doomed liner and were lost, the real Lennons faded into the background, still very much alive. This would then raise two possibilities about the genuine Lennons:

1.. that they eventually did marry and produce offspring, or

2.. that they continued as brother and sister; back in the Irish midlands, as mentioned by the caller to RTE.

The fact that Denis and Mary DID exist was no longer in dispute. Records of the British Red Cross, which had just come into Geoff Whitfield's possession, showed that despite their feelings about Denis, his parents claimed £10 from the Titanic Relief Fund in respect of his loss.

This did not necessarily prove the couple actually were lost; only that two passengers, CARRYING TICKETS IN THE NAMES OF DENIS AND MARY LENNON were lost.

Indeed, at that stage of my investigations, something else seemed to suggest that it was Arthur Stenning, not Denis Lennon who boarded the vessel... i.e., the fact that he was described on the passenger list as a 'labourer' which, indeed, Arthur was. An apprentice storekeeper such as Denis would be most unlikely to demote himself in that way.

There was yet another pointer that made me wonder if what we were dealing with here was not mere supposition, but genuine possibility. It was our man's entry down near the bottom of the passenger lists of those setting off from Queenstown.

Something felt not quite right. Namely, the name. The Irish spelling of Denis usually has only one n; whereas the English version has two.

The name on the passenger list appeared with two n's... which would suggest that this was an Englishman who boarded the vessel. Or, at least, an English person who signed the documents.

Lucy, for example, would never have considered spelling the name Denis other than with the double n... any more than she would have given any thought to the occupation of her escort.

Who, among the authorities on that very busy April morning, would have bothered to check on the quirky spelling of a name, or the nature of a steerage passenger's employment? English or Irish, labourer or assistant storekeeper, what did any of it matter, as long as the emigrants were fit to sail and had the necessary fare? . .

The question was raised as to whether one, or both, of the names might be found among the lists of missing persons; but a search through back numbers of the Police Gazette yielded nothing. Having spent some considerable time checking through mountains of yellowing pages, Andrew Selby, a leading regression researcher, discovered several gaps in London Metropolitan copies covering the years 1910 to 1914.

Switching his attention to The Newspaper Library at Collindale, he searched through every week for the entire year 1912, but again, neither name was listed. All this told us is that neither Lucy nor Arthur was wanted for police questioning.

Beyond that, their absence from the columns was inconclusive. The Stenning family, being travellers, would probably not have known where Arthur was at any given time, so would have had no reason to report him missing.

In any case, the fee of eight shillings (40p) per entry would, presumably, have been beyond their means. At that time, it would have represented a great deal of money to a family of their class.

Hearsay evidence*[1] led us to understand that Lucy's father was well aware of her companion's identity and their ultimate destination. He had, allegedly, written his daughter off. . .

Lucy's birth was documented as having taken place in Market Street, Newton. No house number was entered either on the certificate or in local street directories where her father's name appeared but, in the hope that my unconscious mind would swing into action, I decided to go there.

The town's one thoroughfare turned out to be called High Street. The place was totally strange to me: I knew for a fact that I had never set foot there (in either life!).

Enquiries at the post office as to whether High Street was formerly Market Street resulted in a resounding no. It never was; Market Street was in Earlestown, a couple of miles away. For some curious reason Earlestown, though considerably larger and of more commercial importance, was still categorised as Newton-leWillows. The two had always been conjoined. In Lucy's day, the entire area would have been known as Newton-in-Makerfield, as specified on her birth certificate.

Local street directories simply confirmed what I already knew: that the Latimers resided in the area for a short period at the end of the 19th century. . .

Would parish records reveal more?

Approaches were made to a variety of churches to determine what, if any, records were available. Not knowing whether the family were practising members of any particular religion, I made contact with the authorities of every church listed in Slater's Directory of Warrington, Earlestown, Widnes and St Helens. Priests and vicars were most helpful, but nothing significant emerged. . .

Something struck me like a bolt from the blue.

Until now, I had not given much thought to the fact that Titanic's chief steward was named Andrew Latimer. In a sudden flash of inspiration, I decided to find out where he came from.

I had an uncanny feeling the information was stored in my unconscious, just waiting to be retrieved. Sure enough, historians at the BTS confirmed my suspicions. He hailed from east Lancashire, same as Lucy!

This regression was beginning to be littered with uncanny coincidences. Investigations would now be necessary to establish (or eliminate) any connection between Andrew and Lucy. He was not her father, I knew: but could he have been an uncle, or some other close relation, as hinted by Lucy?

It had already been established that Titanic's chief steward was born in 1857, but his place of birth still needed to be determined. He was known to have spent much of his life in Earlestown, married twice, fathered several children and, at some stage, taken up residence in Liverpool.

It was still my contention that there was a family link between this man and the girl who shared his name, his Lancashire connections and his voyage aboard the doomed liner.

If this were so, had the family relationship been responsible for the choice of trans-Atlantic vessel? Perhaps; although on the flip side of the coin, would a girl be likely to elope on board a ship where her uncle held a high-ranking position?

Probably not, unless she did not know him very well and was unaware of his ranking, or his presence on board. Or, she might not have tumbled to the truth until it was too late to do anything about it; except wish she had never stepped aboard... and try to avoid him.

The most likely explanation was that the elopers were booked to travel on another vessel, and either switched or were switched, to Titanic at the last minute. A long-running coal strike had caused confusion for several shipping companies and their agents. Many ships had been put out of service, necessitating an eleventh-hour transfer of passengers. .

Andrew Latimer's obituary in the Newton and Earlestown Guardian shortly after the sinking, gave his date of birth as January 31, 1857; which was confirmed by St Catherine's House registers[*2] His mother married twice and ran a business in Market Street, where 'my' Latimers lived.

Titanic's chief steward also married twice. The children of his first wife were named George and Madge. Those of his second were Andrew, John, William and Jean: the latter of whom was born three months after the tragedy.

No details were provided about either wife, other than that the first (who died) came from Earlestown, the second (who survived him) from Liverpool.

Initial researches into Andrew Latimer's background were conducted in 1992 (to commemmorate the 80th anniversary of the sinking) by Steve Rigby, joint Honorary Secretary of the BTS. At the time, the sole survivors among Andrew Latimer's children were John and Jean (now Mrs Walmsley).

By the time of my enquiries, John was unavailable, but Jean told me as much as she knew. Her grandfather Robert, had been employed by the railways. He had dropped dead on the platform at Carlisle, where he was station master.

Mrs Walmsley knew little, or nothing, about his children (her aunts and uncles) and, on the subject of her father, apologised for being unable to answer the many personal questions with which I had bombarded her.

'You must remember that I am now 84 and was born two months after my father's death,' she observed.[*3]

Never having known him, Mrs Walmsley had maintained little contact with that side of the family, but she very kindly made approaches to elderly relatives on my behalf. As she had expected, they were no wiser than herself.

It was very good of the elderly lady to go to such trouble and I did appreciate her efforts, but the frustrating fact was that no-one could tell me anything about Lucy or her parents, Thomas and Eunice.

Just as I was preparing to explore other avenues, Steve Rigby turned up trumps. Robert Latimer, he told me, had travelled extensively in his railway career moves. As a result, his children's births had occured in a variety of places: the youngest having been born in Tebay.

Steve's sources were unable to supply the name of Robert's youngest child, but it coul Only have been Thomas. I had documentation to prove it.*[4]

THERE WAS NO DOUBT IN MY MIND NOW THAT MY ALTER-EGO WAS THE NIECE OF ANDREW LATIMER, CHIEF STEWARD OF RMS TITANIC.

I was equally convinced that Andrew Latimer had nothing whatever to do with the presence of Lucy and her partner on the ship.

Whether we could assume that Andrew's father (Lucy's grandfather), the station master Robert Latimer, had any connection with St Kew railway - the station house of which stood at the gates of Lanarth - was another matter . .

The 1891 census for Market Street, Earlestown gave Thomas Latimer's house number as 121 and his profession as 'superintendent for insurance'. Eunice was described as a music teacher. Lucy's name was recorded too, but there was no mention of Alice (who became Mrs Lewis) but then, on her own admission she was not born until 1903, by which time the family would have been well away from here. But there was a servant girl.

HER NAME WAS SARAH JANE, JUST AS MRS LEWIS HAD STATED.*[5]

NOTES, CHAPTER 27

*1 See chapter nine.

*2 Birth registers for first quarter 1857 show Latimer, Andrew, b.Lancaster; Vol.8e, P.350.

*3 Author's correspondence.

*4 1891 Census shows Thomas Latimer's place of birth as Courthouse Lane, Tebay

*5 See chapter nine.

Chapter 28

My next course of action was to seek out Lucy's birthplace and, if the property was still standing, discover what - if any impressions or sentiments it might stir up.

Market Street led from Earlestown's main thoroughfare to a long, tree-lined road of residential properties. Walking away from the town centre, I found odd numbers on the left.

And this was really weird.

Approaching number 121, I suddenly knew it would be still there and, despite the fact that the properties lining the road were a mix of architectural style and period, I knew exactly how this one would look. It would stand adjoining the end house in a Victorian red-bricked terrace.

It did. Something even more uncanny struck me as I gazed at the house: namely, the similarities between this property and the very first house I bought in Liverpool.

Not only were they roughly the same age, but they were similarly positioned in their terrace: both being just one away from the corner; in the same direction. Neither was graced with a lawn or garage.

No disrespect to the present occupiers is intended when I remark on the ordinariness of these two properties. With hindsight, I could not help wondering why I bought the one I had, about 12 miles away.

Had something drawn me to it: some inner force of which I was then totally unaware? In the event, it proved an unwise choice.

For reasons which it would be neither relevant nor appropriate to dwell upon here, I grew to loathe that first house. It was not until circumstances changed and I moved miles away that the dark clouds hovering over it began to lift.

Was it a similar story for the Latimers? Was that what led them to Cornwall? Or was it pure coincidence that I was drawn, decades later, to a house of similar size and style to the one where Lucy was born? . .

While I was chasing around Lancashire, Rita Warmington was chasing around Cornwall. Her latest news was disappointing. There was, she reported, no evidence to substantiate the rumours surrounding Mrs Latimer's demise.

"Unfortunately, we vary rarely keep records of 'suspicious incidents' at CFHS: by the very nature of our Society, we must be careful to supply only proven information because of the offence we might give to members of other families using our services either as members, or as the public," she explained.

Her request from the Cornwall Record Office for access to Coroners' Inquests had drawn a blank. However, all was not lost: a search through old editions of Kelly's Commercial Directory for Devon and Cornwall revealed two familiar names among the lists of private residents. One was that of a Mrs Latimer, (no first name) living in St Kew Highway; the other was a Mr Thomas Latimer.

The 1883 edition (unfortunately, a decade too early for our purposes) showed Mrs Latimer living in the house then known as Newton (Lanarth); Thomas, in Exeter.

Mrs Warmington, so skilled at digging up obscure facts, concluded with an exciting disclosure: "Land tax records for St Kew show that the Latimers were not owners. At the time of their stay, Lanarth was offering apartments to rent."

THIS WAS A BRAND NEW, AND HIGHLY SIGNIFICANT, PIECE OF INFORMATION.

If, in the years to come, Lucy and her relatively humble family had rented a couple of rooms in that lovely house, and the child had 'ideas above her station', might she not have boasted wildly about her parentage and social circumstances?

Was it so outlandish to conclude that a little girl from EARLestown should claim noble ancestry (as she kept insisting in early regressions: 'my father's a baron')? Far from being daunted by the splendour of her surroundings, could she not have been her own little Lady of the Manor?

Lady Lucie of Lanarth. . . .

Chapter 29

It was now more than five years since I had begun my researches. Where it was all leading, I still had no idea. Lucy's date and place of birth were known, her date and place of death presumed; but a big question mark hung over the circumstances of her life. Apart from the information obtained through regression and various official records, there was little in the way of human interest to fill in the personal details.

To ensure that the Lucy Latimer, born in July, 1890 was 'my' Lucy, I still needed to seek out any living relatives she might have and put my theories to them.

If this were NOT 'my' Lucy, the girl whose birth certificate I held might have died in infancy, or at any time other than in the icy waters of the North Atlantic on that memorable night, 83 years ago. She might have lived on, married (or remained single) and died in old age. It was just conceivable that she might still be alive, aged 105!

Had any of these possibilities been established as fact, my entire case would have had to be thrown overboard and everything in the regression with it.

While there was no proof yet that Lucy was who I believed her to be, it was a distinct possibility. Admittedly, most of my evidence was negative, but it was better than none at all.

I wanted more. Newshounds are no different from any other hounds. If there is still some juicy particle to extract from a bone, they carry on chewing.

To satisfy my voracious appetite for facts, the ever-helpful BTS historians threw me some extra morsels.

Steve Rigby's latest researches had disclosed that Andrew Latimer's parents - Robert and Margaret (nee Tate) - had 10 children. I was given to understand that after Robert's sudden death (in 1860) on the platform of Carlisle railway station, his widow remarried one William Johnson, who ran a public house near the border town of Lockerbie.*[1] Margaret was widowed for the second time in 1875. Then she moved to Earlestown and ran another business very close to where Thomas (her son?) later set up home.

There, the Latimer researches ended. Lucy appeared to have no living relatives - or none prepared to come forward. .

I hoped for better news from the Irish front and, sure enough, it came.

In a telephone call from America, Bob Bracken updated me on what he knew about the Lennons. He had, he told me, met a member of the family, Jimmy, during a recent visit to the British Isles. Apparently, Denis was born in 1891, in the parish of Curracreaghan, near Ballymahon. A peek at the map of Ireland showed the town to be situated in Co Longford; not far from Athlone, where Denis had been employed.

His parents, William and Bridget (nee Mullen) ran a family farm and had aspirations for their son. No information was available about the mysterious Mary, other than that which I already had. They disapproved of her.

Jimmy's address was unknown, but I did not anticipate any difficulty in locating him. The beauty of Irish country towns is that everyone knows everyone else.

I would find this man, even if it involved jetting over there, complete with sniffer dog. . .

It was vitally important for me to make contact with the Lennons, but - and this was a BIG but - I could not predict how the Irish family might react to the idea of a stranger probing into the affairs of one of their ancestors; particularly a stranger with such an offbeat tale to tell. Knowing only too well the Catholic church's view on life after death, I suddenly began to question the wisdom of my proposed approach. Would Jimmy Lennon prove hostile? . .

My fears were unfounded.

Located through Longford's main public library, Jimmy responded with not just one, but two friendly letters in the same post. The first contained confirmation of Bob Bracken's story, as he himself believed the facts to have been at the time of their meeting. The second contained copies of baptismal certificates for Denis, his four sisters and two brothers and a map of the parish, showing the extent of the Lennons' 20-acre farm.

My correspondent explained that, although not a direct descendant of Denis, he certainly was related. He went on to explain that he (Jimmy) worked as a researcher with a genealogical company, which put him in a privileged position to access records.

"However, these records are only available to us for a period up until 1890," he told me; the reason being that a number of people were employed on social welfare schemes and sensitive information like that of illegitimate births could be traced to descendants living in the area. "The clergy have made a point of not allowing access after the aforementioned date," he concluded.

Jimmy later related how, as a small boy, he used to sit by the big open hearth in his grandmother's kitchen and listen to the elderly John Lennon tell of his brother's sad fate.

"I understood that Denis married - or was planning to marry - a girl of whom his parents did not approve and that the couple were, in fact, booked on another liner but due to the coal strike were offered places, at the last minute, on the Titanic.

"There have been many features in our local newspaper relating to Longford passengers but for some strange reason the names of Denis Lennon or Mary were never mentioned," reflected Jimmy. He himself believed that they did not marry, because no records could be found.

Over the years, a variety of rumours had been circulating about Mary's identity. One was that it was her father who employed Denis and that it was he, not Denis's parents, who disapproved so strongly of the match.

Jimmy still believed it was the Lennons who ejected their offspring, but was less convinced about Mary's being the shopkeeper's daughter. He planned to investigate further. .

Encouraged by most of what I had been told and, hoping that the final clue to the mystery of the missing elopees was about to be revealed, I ventured to invite Jimmy's views on the regression, as well as on the possible link between my alter-ego and his own romantic antecedent. Having pointed out the discrepancies about the spellings of Denis's name *[2] and the apparent confusion about his job, I wondered if he agreed with my latest theory? Did he think it possible that a couple of imposters had made the ill-fated trip in the name of the Lennons?

I wondered if, in his capacity as a professional genealogist, he could trace the very elderly Denis and Mary Lennon referred to (as living in the Irish Midlands, like himself) by the RTE listener.*[3] If they were still alive and willing to speak, could the genealogist ascertain whether THEY were the Denis and Mary who headed for Titanic all those years ago?

Could he establish whether their tickets sold to, or stolen by, another couple about the same age as themselves? It was a long shot and might lead nowhere, but I was clutching at straws.

Jimmy might not be able to locate the two geriatrics. In view of their great age, one or both, might now be dead. If he did locate them, they might not be the couple I wanted. If they were, they might be unwilling or unable to speak. So many ifs... They might claim to know nothing about the Titanic and explode my theory out of hand.

Then again, how would we ever know whether they were telling the truth or not? It would be perfectly understandable for a couple who presumably shied away from identifying themselves in the wake of the tragedy, to continue lying low.

Who could blame them for wanting to spend their final years in peace? But wouldn't it be fantastic if they were located, spoken to and revealed their identity, confirming that they did indeed switch places with a young English couple eloping under circumstances not dissimilar to their own?..

Jimmy's next letter professed absolute fascination with the regression. Though taken aback at the thought of Denis and Mary not having made their fateful trip, he could offer nothing concrete regarding the suggested link between Lucy and Denis. Nor could he supply any information about the geriatric Denis and Mary allegedly living (or having lived) in the Irish midlands.

On second thoughts, I was not convinced it would have been such a good idea to disturb them; even though Jimmy did confirm that Longford - so heavily populated with Lennons - was indeed in that region of Ireland.

About my postulation that Denis might not have been aboard Titanic at all, he pointed out that the Lennon elders had strong reservations. In the belief that Denis had drowned so tragically all those years ago, they still remembered him in Requiem Masses.

Enclosed with Jimmy's latest letter was a photocopied Latin entry from an old Catholic register, documenting the birth of Dionysius on December 9, 1891.[*4]

The idea of Mary's not being 'good enough' for Denis's parents was definitely in dispute, and my genealogist friend put forward a new and much more exciting theory.

While he still believed that Denis and Mary were eloping on Titanic, and that they were unmarried at the time of the tragedy: "I am now almost certain that she was very upper-class and that it was HER family who disapproved of the relationship," he declared.

This was creepy. Apart from the fact that Denis had more social status than Arthur, the story of the Irish runaways was becoming more like that of my two every day. . .

While Jimmy was digging ever further into his ancestral roots, I was reflecting upon whether it would be too far-fetched to imagine that Lucy and her original escort parted company and that she ran off instead with Denis... thus making HER the mysterious 'Mary' for whom we were searching.

She was not exactly upper-class, but she did like to think of herself in that way. Lady Lucie, remember... and the claims about her father? Also, there was her inexplicable knowledge about the barony of Latymer.

Ah, but would she have been the type to reject her original love for another? Who knows? If she was and she did, it would not be the first time a girl backed off at the last minute and bolted with someone else.

How and when she met Denis (if we accept the likelihood that she did) might never be established; though a possibility was revolving in my brain.[*5]

(A thought: what a wonderful time the pair of them must have had in Queenstown; I, on visiting the town, knew happiness that was almost tangible.)

Such a union might account for Lucy's unco-operative attitude in regression. Questions about who she was with invariably resulted in answers varying from coyness, to irritability, to pretentiousness ('I'm with my retinue') to downright rudeness ('Mind your own business').

Were these clever responses Miss Mystery's attempts to put us off the scent, determined to let no-one tumble to her last great secret?

I had not yet resolved the puzzle, but I suspected I was tantalisingly close.

NOTES, CHAPTER 29

*1 Lockerbie made international headlines in December 1988, when a bomb exploded aboard Pan Am flight 103 and its 259 passengers were blown out of the sky; devastating the town centre and much of its surrounding area.

*2 The name Denis is spelt with one n on the baptismal certificate, as indeed it is on Jimmy Lennon's letters and those of all other Irish correspondence.

*3 See chapter 26

*4 Entry number 89

*5 To be fully expounded in the final chapter.

Chapter 30

Cheshire, England, Spring 1996.

After six years of searching for clues, what is the situation? In keeping with my profession of investigative journalist, I have spent hours checking out my sources, chasing leads, digging up and examining anything - however obscure - that might be relevant to this regression.

To begin with, the sceptic might ask if the whole remarkable story might not be due to an over-active imagination.

My response would be that, while Lucy certainly did seem to be a highly imaginative girl, I would strenuously deny having made it all up: dreamed it up, yes; much of it having come through in the form of nightmares, but no cheating (unconscious or otherwise) has been involved.

I personally had no contact with, or conscious knowledge of Earlestown, Lanarth, or Cobh. Yet the character who emerged during regression was vaguely familiar with the first and had intimate knowledge of the other two. She also knew rather more about RMS Titanic than I ever did in my conscious, or waking, state.

All right, so the links between Lucy's birth at Earlestown and her death in the North Atlantic are tenuous, to say the least. The only common denominator I have been able to discover is Andrew Latimer, chief steward, whom I believe to have been her uncle.

Can we prove that the Lancashire-born Lucy Latimer is the same person who grew up in Lanarth?

Not categorically, no. The evidence is almost all circumstantial; though there are plenty of positive pointers:

1. The strange sensations attached to the Earlestown house, associated with her odd references in regression to an earl, or earls.
2. The servant girl, Sarah Jane: a common factor to both Lancashire and Cornwall.
3. The companion, Arthur Stenning, who accompanied her at least on the first leg of her journey and
4. A set of very vivid memories and images of Lanarth; most of which have been substantiated, although admittedly there are gaps.

While none of this conclusively proves that she ever lived at Lanarth, we do know that the house was let into apartments around the time in question and that, although neither Lucy nor her parents appear on the records by name, a family of Latimers DID live there.

Also, we have hearsay evidence of young Miss Latimer running off with a labourer named Arthur Stenning in the general direction of Titanic.

How do we know Lucy boarded the ship at Queenstown and not Southampton, as was originally suggested?

We do not, but can anyone offer an alternative explanation for my recognising so much about the Irish port and its environs when I had never been there in this life, and for the spooky feelings as I stood near the White Star Pier.

What about her childish claim that her father was a baron?

He clearly was not and I can offer no rational explanation for her wild boast.

I cannot begin to explain my (subconscious) knowledge about the barony of Latymer going into abeyance. Nor, although 'my' Lady Lucie Latymer insisted on spelling both her Christian and surname thus, is there any proven connection between herself and the real Lady Lucie Latymer of the 16th century: daughter of the Earl of Worcester.

Put it down to coincidence again that it was yet another Lady Lucy (-this time spelt the conventional way) who was responsible for the Barony of Latymer going into abeyance in 1609 when she died, leaving four daughters but no son and heir. By the time it came out of abeyance in 1911, the subject of this book would certainly have been around, though what on earth made her think HER father had any claim to the title, I cannot imagine.

Apart from confirmation about the abeyance of the barony of Latymer, how much documented evidence is there regarding the life of Lucy, as portrayed through the regression?

Quite a lot, actually, considering the difficulties of researching a character who had no offspring and who went all out to evade those who attempted to pursue her:

1. Birth certificate, Lucy;
2. Birth certificate Arthur;
3. Entry of Lucy's father's name on the Earlestown census returns, local street directories, St Catherine's House registers;
4. Confirmation of a pond having once formed part of the grounds at Lanarth and of a railway station at its gates;
5. Confirmation that Latimers did live at Lanarth around the period in question.
6. Recently-acquired information about the young lady who eloped with Denis Lennon, whose circumstances exactly matched those of our heroine.

On the completion of this research project, therefore, I am left in no doubt that Lucy did exist; that she spent most of her life at Lanarth, ran off with the labourer, Arthur Stenning, intending elopment but later switched her affection to Denis Lennon, with whom she boarded Titanic for their double date with destiny. But I am still not 100 percent certain. In these sort of cases, no-one ever can be.

Piecing the smaller clues together involves examining the miscellany of general impressions, some mere fleeting shadows. These tell us that, although Lucy and her escort ended up on Titanic, it was not the ship originally booked, and Jimmy Lennon did say that Denis was to have travelled on another vessel but transferred to Titanic because of the coal strike. I was also now firmly convinced that the man with whom Lucy spent her final days was not her original escort.

Then there was the business of that vaguely-familiar face among the uniformed officers.

Very little is known of her relationship with Denis because that was precisely how Lucy herself wanted it. All we can do is attempt to slot the various fragments into place.

Let me present a possible scenario.

Lucy set off with Stennie and together they journeyed to Ireland, where they were soon lost in the middle of the country. Things began to go wrong between them. Away from familiar surroundings, the relationship became strained.

An imperious young madam, Lucy found Arthur indecisive and irresponsible. She wanted to settle down, but his feet were itchy. Born of travelling stock, the wanderlust was inbred.

After much mental anguish and self-recrimination on the part of both, they went their separate ways.

No details are known of when or where she met the man with whom she spent her final days. That was something over which she really did pull the veil of secrecy.

From here on, I had to rely on even flimsier impressions and vaguer memories, because she had almost - though not completely - blocked out her 'misdeeds'. It is amazing what a guilty conscience can do to the mind... even in a previous incarnation!

I formed the impression that Lucy obliterated most of the details of her personal life from the moment she left her English home, to the point where she was in Queenstown, preparing for her sea journey in the company of the man to whom she had completely lost her heart. The time between her parting with 'Stennie' and her presence in Queenstown with 'Dennie' must remain shrouded in mystery. . .

While she was not terribly well endowed with grey matter, she was not altogether dim. It would not have taken her long to realise that the name Lucy was so unusual in the Irish countryside that it could draw attention to her. That was the last thing she wanted.

Having discovered that every other girl in the vicinity was called Mary, she decided to join their ranks. The surname did pose something of a problem. Local family names were totally foreign to her, most being utterly unpronouncable.

Lucy (now Mary) overcame the difficulty by asking the few people with whom she deigned to communicate, to address her simply as Miss Mary; thus continuing to give her acquaintances the impression of a well-connected family background. Miss Mary was a demotion from Lady Mary (or Lady Lucy as people at home called her), but it couldn't be helped. Protection of her anonymity was the most important issue at stake.

No one must know who she really was. Only herself. Oh, and God, she supposed, when she bothered to give Him any thought.

In one of the regression sessions when those around observed that, as Lucy, I was particularly quiet, it was because of my alter-ego's pensive mood. Attempting to blank out the details of what had gone on before her meeting with Denis, she was allowing her mind to wander back briefly over the events of her life thus far: the sudden demise of Mama, the awfulness of Papa and his stupid companion; her own silliness at leaving home when she knew she shouldn't have; her brief liaison with Stennie.

I felt myself smile as the 'other me' mused on how sparkingly beautiful everything had suddenly become. Now that she had found her new love - and this time it really WAS love - the sun would shine forever.

Lucy did not consider herself a fast young lady, but her meeting with Denis had been wonderful beyond relief. Wasn't it remarkable, too, that the names of her two companions should be so similar? First, Stennie. Now, Dennie.

She would speak of this love to no-one, whatever the circumstances. Even The Voice must think she was still with Stennie. . .

Can anyone give credence to the Stennie/Dennie switchover?

Yes, let me hand over to Jimmy Lennon for a report on the latest findings.

"I can now totally discard the theory of Mary being the daughter of Denis's boss," he told me.

"This rumour is entirely without foundation. Investigations into contemporary owners of the shop in Athlone show no record of any daughter answering to 'Mary's' description.

Jimmy was therefore much more inclined to agree that the lady was not local. It strengthened the possibility of her having been (or claiming to have been) highborn and possibly disinherited.

But why should the circumstances of their romance be clouded in mystery? Could it have been because 'Mary' was an English Protestant?

"That certainly could account for their association being hushed up," he told me. Denis's family, all good, practising Catholics, numbered several priests. Traditionally, the idea of mixed marriages was frowned upon in such communities.

In passing, he also mentioned having made an odd discovery.

Longford county census for 1901 contained an entry for a family named Latimer (with a daughter, called Mary), but the idea of these Latimers being 'very upper class' can be discounted. The father was a postman. Was he yet another of Lucy's uncles? Could it have been during a visit to that household that she met her Denis?

That is something we shall never know. .

Throughout this research, one half of my mind was focussed on Arthur Stenning (Stennie), the other on Denis Lennon (Dennie). It now seemed almost certain that Lucy had an association with both. Was it any wonder her guilty conscience clouded the information provided in regression?

I don't doubt that she set off from Lanarth with Arthur Stenning, but I believe that the man with whom she stepped on board Titanic was not he.

All the signs are that it could only have been Denis.

I feel sure too that, circumstances being what they were, sex never once entered the relationship between these two. He, being a thoroughly wholesome chap, would have believed in waiting until after the marriage ceremony. She, despite being such a little hothead, came through as naive in the extreme.

What became of Arthur? Who knows? Perhaps he found a companion more worthy of his love.

If he's with us again, I hope he's happy. .

'So sinks the day star in the ocean bed.'

Milton, John: Lycidas

John P. Eaton's conclusions...

What we already know - or do not know - about those actually aboard Titanic is fascinating enough. We now know that among the liner's passengers there were well upwards of fifty whose names were misspelled, noted but not named, or deliberately falsified. Even people with but a passing interest in the subject know who among the latter were 'Mr and Mrs Morgan' or 'E Rosenbaum' or even Baron Alfred van Drachstedt'. There are many other false names known to Titanic scholars with whom real people can be associated.

Now, to 'Phillips' and 'Wilkinson', to 'Wennerstrom' and 'Hoffman' can be added a name hitherto 'unknown amongst the unknowns'. . . that of Miss Lucy Latimer.

Thank you for taking us on this journey, Monica, and especially for sharing with us your own vital role in it. .

THE END

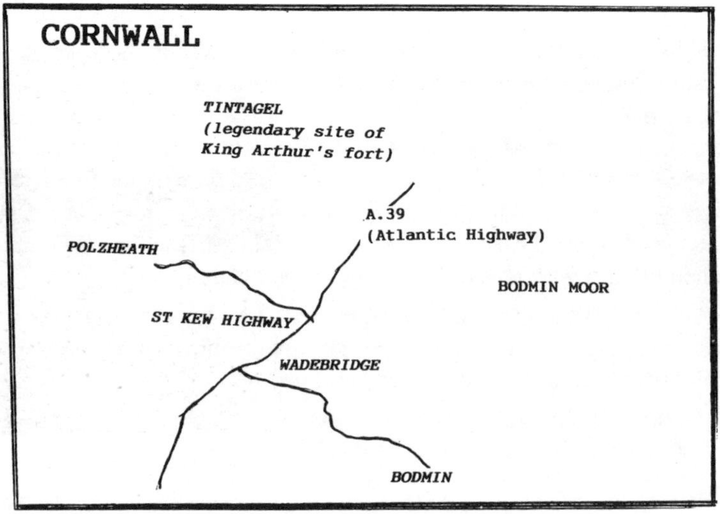

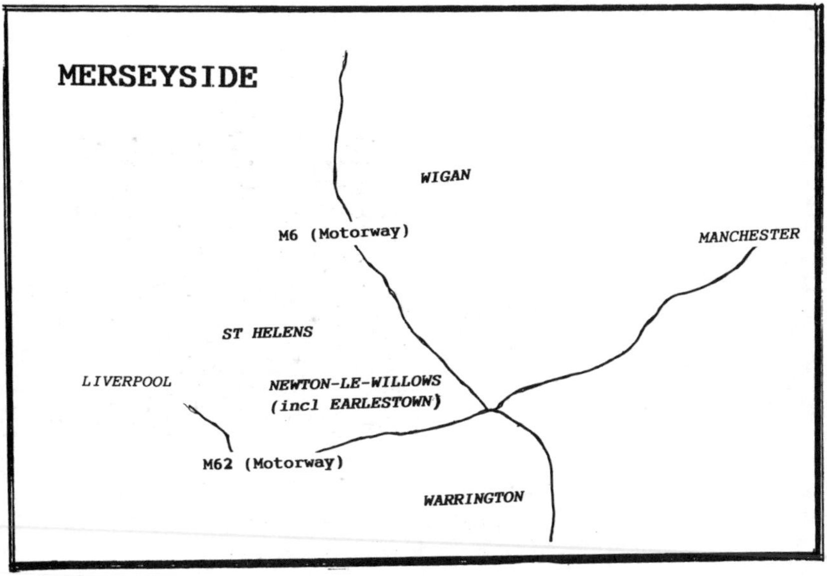

Maps drawn by the author

Joe Keeton,
hypnotherapist.

Monica O'Hara
all ready for regression!

Sight of still, deep water, causes nightmares before pre-birth regression therapy removes the phobia.

Apart from the cathedral spire, which was not there in 1912, this could be Lucy's last sight of land.

All four pictures from the author's collection.

HANDS OFF THE TITANIC!

MONICA HARDING O 'HARA

(Countyvise, £3. 95)

* 'This book is utterly fascinating and treads ground on which no-one has ever laid a foot.'

  John P Eaton, internationally-acclaimed Titanic historian and author, New York.

* 'Another dimension for Titanic buffs/researchers...An unusual and refreshing viewpoint. I highly recommend this important little book.'

  Karen Kamuda, Titanic Commutator, Indian Orchard.

* 'It has all the hallmarks of a classic detective story.'

  Steve Taylor, BBC TV 'North West Tonight'.

* 'A fascinating read... it throws a whole new light on the story of Titanic.' Alan Doulby, *BBC Radio Wales.*

* 'A fascinating new slant to the mountain of literature on the sinking of Titanic.' Paul Burnell, *Catholic Pictorial.*

* 'An interesting, fascinating book, and one that lends itself to bedtime reading, or whenever there is an odd time to spare.'

  Dungarvan Observer.

* 'An intriguing insight into the people connected with the story.'

  Peter Grant, Liverpool Echo.

* 'There would seem to be little more to say, but Monica Harding O'Hara has come up with a fascinating new dimension.'

  Alan Domville, Warrington Guardian.

* 'I feel sure that if father knew about this book, he would be greatly pleased.'

  Stanley Lord, son of Captain Stanley Lord, of the ss Californian, to whose memory the book was dedicated.